Grace
Wahira

a book

11-10
48-49
18-19
54-55
62-63

Made in HEAVEN

"Learning the secret of flight from a bird was a good deal like learning the secret of magic from a magician."
– Orville Wright

Ray Comfort
Best-selling author, TV co-host

Jeffrey Seto (B. Eng.)
Aerospace Engineer – Experimental Research & Design

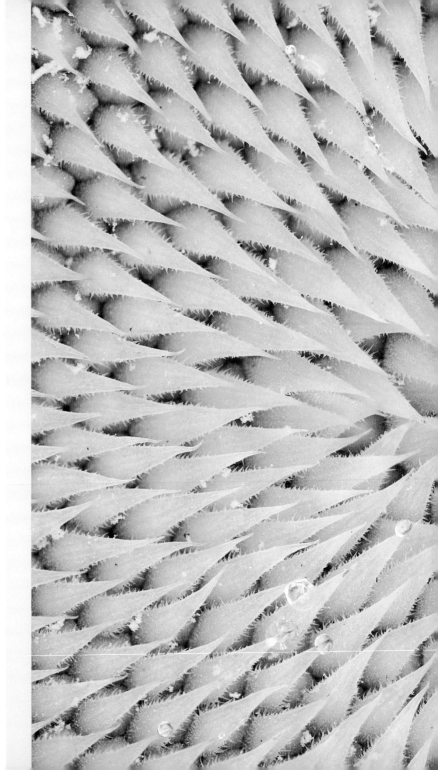

First printing: October 2012

Copyright © 2012 by Ray Comfort & Jeffrey Seto. All rights reserved. No part of this book may be used or reproduced in any manner whatsoever without written permission of the publisher, except in the case of brief quotations in articles and reviews. For information write:
Master Books®, P.O. Box 726, Green Forest, AR 72638

Master Books® is a division of the New Leaf Publishing Group, Inc.

ISBN: 978-0-89051-669-0
eISBN: 978-1-61458-265-6
Library of Congress Number: 2012947960

Cover and Interior Design by Diana Bogardus

Unless otherwise noted, Scripture quotations are from the English Standard Version of the Bible.

Please consider requesting that a copy of this volume be purchased by your local library system.

Printed in the United States of America

Please visit our website for other great titles: www.masterbooks.net

For information regarding author interviews,
please contact the publicity department at (870) 438-5288

Master Books®
A Division of New Leaf Publishing Group
www.masterbooks.net

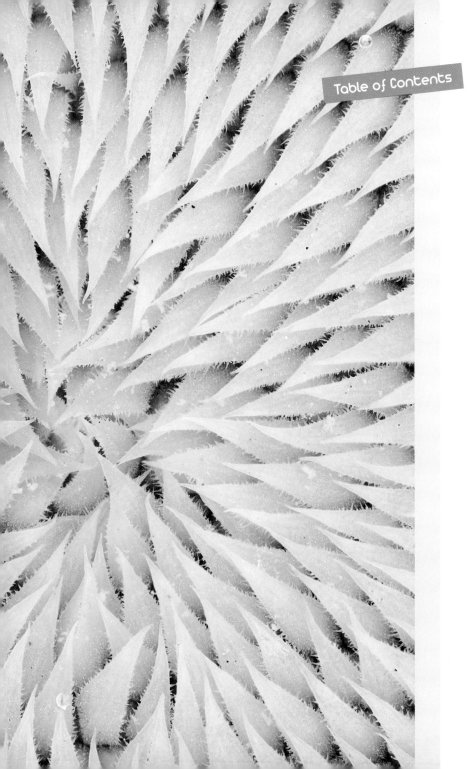

Table of Contents

FOREWORD

My first experience in complex design began with my dad. He was always the guy who could fix anything and was forever tinkering in his workshop. He worked for several companies and had several inventions before working as a national products safety inspector.

As a young boy I enjoyed seeing how things work and began deconstructing them to see the mechanics. I was employed part-time during high school at an auto shop and wanted to transition it to a full-time job. I had no plans to attend college or university.

My dad, however, encouraged me to take a college course. He valued education, and I respected him, so I took a two-year course in avionics. I loved it and fully immersed myself in basic science and electronic theory.

During one of my courses, I asked my professor to expound on the current theorem we were discussing. He replied that expanded understanding could only be acquired by attending university. So I applied to study aerospace engineering the next semester. To date, it's been 22 years and three different countries that I've been blessed to work in as an aerospace engineer.

Engineering is a complex and dynamic field that drives our modern culture with technological advances. They make our lives better, according to *Merriam Webster*, "through the application of science and mathematics by which the properties of matter and the sources of energy in nature are made useful to people." In short: engineers discover better, faster, and more innovative new products that improve our lives.

Engineering is imagination-and design-driven. Nowhere is this more evident than the study of the natural world applied to the science of engineering. Engineers have long examined God's creation to understand and mimic complex and proven mechanics of design. They have plumbed the depths of the natural world, encompassing insects to plants to man in search of wisdom and insight.

The simplicity yet intricacy of how God's designs work and how He manufactures complexity in nature astounds and inspires engineers in hypotheses and designs that could not be formed otherwise. We can only marvel, admire, and maybe copy some examples our Creator has left for us to discover.

— Jeffrey Seto, B.Eng

"Worthy are you, our Lord and God,
to receive glory and honor and power,
for you created all things,
and by your will they existed and were created."

–Revelation 4:11

INTRODUCTION

"In the beginning, God created the heavens and the earth."

–Genesis 1:1

THE SIGN OF DESIGN

When skeptics ask for a "sign" that proves the existence of a Creator, the sign to look for is the sign of nature's design. When Sir Isaac Newton said that atheism was "sense-less," he chose his words carefully. Those who look at the unspeakably wonderful design of nature and don't see the hand of the Designer are truly sense-less. They're not using their God-given senses of sight, sound, touch, taste, and smell. Nature screams of God and, for some reason, they turn a deaf ear, a blind eye, and a closed mouth.

Let's play the game of atheism for a moment by surmising that there's no evidence that the book you are holding had an author or a designer. There was nothing, and for some reason paper evolved. So did glue, ink, and cardboard. Then, over millions of years, the book fell together into a spine, a beautifully self-designed cover, saddle-stitched pages with consecutive numbers on each page. Then intelligent information fell from somewhere and formed itself into straight lines of text and coherent sentences with bold headings and indented paragraphs — all in perfectly spelled English. But there's more to this fantasy. Each photo you see in the book evolved from nothing into a beautiful picture, with text explaining each one.

What sort of senseless person could believe that? An atheist could. I have talked to many atheists who believe that given "time" anything is possible. There is a word more descriptive than Newton's "senseless" for such a person. The Bible says that he is a "fool" (see Psalm 14:1).

THE DOOR OF LEARNING

We often boast of human beings "creating" different things, and yet we can't create a heart, a living hair, a frog, or even a grain of sand . . . from nothing. We can re-create (using God's material), but in reality we cannot create a thing. That's God's business, and when we realize that, it is humbling — and nothing opens eyes like humility. Humility is the door of learning. A know-it-all can't learn a thing.

Humility is also the key to reconciliation. This is so evident on the freeway. Have you ever been cut off by a thoughtless driver? You fume at him, but when the driver looks directly at you, lifts his hand in a humble gesture of contrition, and mouths, "I'm so sorry," your anger dissipates just as quickly. You feel like calling out, "That's okay! I understand. I do silly things myself all the time. Let's be friends!" Humility reconciles man to man, and man to God.

Psalm 34:2 talks about the humble man or woman and his or her reaction to praise. It says, "My soul shall make her boast in the Lord: the humble shall hear thereof, and be glad." If you want to see pride rear its ugly head, boast about something God did for you — perhaps something you believe was an answer to prayer, and listen to the proud heart attribute it to luck, coincidence, fate . . . anything but God.

Or talk about how awesome God is in His creation to a proud person, and listen to him give Mother Nature praise. There are even some who would rather believe that nothing created everything and give no praise at all to anything than give God one ounce of glory.

THE ANT SCHOOL

Let's humbly look at one tiny part of creation. Solomon encouraged the sluggard to go to the ant and consider her ways, and be wise. If we do that we will see that the tiny insect is incredibly industrious. We rarely see one standing still. It's good (and wise) to be inspired to work by the ant's example; however, there's another reason we should go to the ant and consider not just her ways but her very being.

There are about 20,000 different types of ants. Consider how they are all similarly designed with three main body parts: the head, the thorax (middle portion), and the abdo-men (rear portion). The outside of its body is covered with a protective armor called the "exoskeleton." Now contemplate how each one has incredibly complex compound eyes, a mouth that can distinguish different foods, amazing claws that grip, feet that walk, an instinct to make a nest, to recognize a mate and procreate, to take care of its young, to identify things that are profitable for the ant hill/farm, and the ability to sleep, eat, and digest food.

Each of the 20,000 different types of ants has a nervous system that contains its multifaceted, tiny, but brilliant brain. Each one has a heart that is a long tube that pumps a special type of blood through its body, as well as an intricate muscle system that works the claws and legs. It has the ability to detect danger and can instantly respond to the call to battle and unify with an army to ward off attackers. It can also unify to attack and completely devour its prey, sometimes in moments.

So who tells the ants to attack in such unity, and where do they get their training to know what to do? The answer is that most of their behavior takes place because they are pre-programmed in their DNA to act the way they do, in the same way that the programming in our DNA tells our blood to clot. However, they do have some schooling taking place, where they learn different skills.

Many animals can learn behaviors by imitation but ants may be the only group apart from mammals where interactive teaching has been observed. A knowledgeable forager of *Temnothorax albipennis* leads a naive nest-mate to newly discovered food by the process of tandem running. The follower obtains knowledge through its leading tutor. Both leader and follower are acutely sensitive to the progress of their partner, with the leader slowing down when the follower lags and speeding up when the follower gets too close. [1]

Perhaps you are thinking, Wow! Ants are incredible! But we should instead be thinking about how utterly incredible God is to have the ability to conceive the thought of the ant, and then to create it.

Do you ever think about God? Do you ever consider how the ant is just a tiny part of the millions of different insects and that they all have amazingly intricate features?

Do you ever think about flies, or eyes, or skies, or birds, nerds, words, or trees, bees, and even knees — with their remarkable ball-and-socket joints and their smoother-than-oil synovial fluid that keeps everything moving efficiently? Have you ever looked deeply into your own eyes in a mirror or studied the dexterity of your hands and thought about how you are "fearfully and wonderfully made"?

Our problem is that we don't consider creation in any real depth, and we give even less thought to the Creator. We are truly blind, and we will stay in that state until we humble ourselves and have our eyes opened through the new birth (see John 3:1–6). When I became a Christian at the age of 22, everything suddenly looked different. I was no longer blind. The trees looked different. The sunrise looked different. I looked at all of nature differently. I saw that every branch, every tree, every leaf was lifting up its arms in praise to the God who made it! The early morning birds sang His praises. The colorful and fragrant flowers radiated with vibrant life and opened their faces to His glory. The tiny ant screamed of the genius of Almighty God. Everything looked different because I was different. I was a new person with a new heart and new desires, having the eyes of my understanding enlightened. In a moment of time I was no longer blind, deaf, and dumb . . . and so my soul is about to make its boast in the Lord. I hope you hear what this book says and are glad — because you look beyond the painting and see the Painter.

—Ray Comfort

1. SWIM LIKE A FISH: COPYING SHARK SCALES

Swimming like a fish might get you on the Olympic swim team, but having a swimsuit that mimics a fish might improve your time there, too. This is the beauty of the science that studies the natural world to find solutions. The shark, for example, is an enigma. It is the killer of the seas and known for its stealth. However, it would not seem to be the natural choice to study swimming like a fish due to its bumpy scales called placoid scales, also known as dermal denticles (skin that looks like teeth).

We generally think that smooth, torpedo-like surfaces allow you to swim like a fish. It's hard to reconcile that the shark's placoid scales would allow smooth swimming, but we know sharks are strong swimmers.

The boundary layer is an area that lies closest to the shark's body and affects how water flows past a body (shark/swimmer). This layer transitions from a laminar (smooth) to a turbulent (rough) flow along the length of the body. The transition from laminar to turbulent flow is inevitable with any moving body, and the area in which it will occur is of greatest value to streamlining a body.

The length of the shark to the region where its body protrudes outward has smooth laminar flow. Normally after any protrusion, flow separation occurs and results in turbulent flow. This transition from laminar to turbulent flow occurs somewhere along the length of the shark.

Engineers calculate and determine the position of this transition and are able to move this transition region further toward the back. The outcome is extended laminar flow, which invariably lessens drag, resulting in a faster-moving object.

Although swimming like a fish is a little more complicated than just the boundary layer, Speedo™ designed FastSkin®, a swimsuit that mimics the shark's placoid scales with a sharp-edged riblet design. Some studies have even suggested that these have no effect since the microstructure of sharks' skin is more complicated and the key to their speed has not been unlocked, but you wouldn't know that by looking at the Olympic teams when these suits were first introduced and swimming speeds were improved. Since then we have seen many advances focused on increasing speed and retaining less water to gain an edge in competitive events such as Olympic trials and the official games.

Made of fabric that mimics sharkskin, Fastskin® remains one of the fastest choices in the pool. Designed to repel water and compress the body.

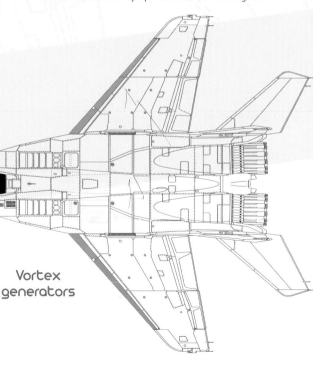

Vortex generators

Placoid scales have also been adapted in aircraft and cars. These "V-shaped" channels in aircraft have been around for a while and are known as vortex generators (VG). When relating to aircraft, VGs are installed on the front third of the upper surface of a wing, which results in a delayed transition (i.e., flow separation) and an increased region of laminar flow, making the airplane move faster. Engineers have been able to increase efficiency on land, in the air, and in the sea when endeavoring to learn from a superior design by a superior designer.

2. BODY ARMOR OF THE FUTURE — STRENGTH OF FISH SCALES

Thoughts of body armor likely conjure up images of a medieval knight donning a rigid and impervious suit of armor. Suits of armor in the Middle Ages were entirely made of steel and formed to the shape of the knight. It effectively offered protection, but the cost was mobility as movement proved heavy and difficult.

The quest for military and law enforcement officers is protective body armor that is flexible, lightweight, and capable of protecting the body from ballistic projectiles. A solution may lie in the Amazon basin of South America. Here resides the native arapaima fish. The arapaima is one of the world's largest freshwater fish and can reach lengths up to 9 feet and weigh up to 440 pounds. It isn't the size but the exterior scales of the fish that has stirred creative new ideas for body armor.

The arapaima scales can reach lengths up to four inches long and are arranged in an overlapping layout along the longitudinal axis of the fish. Its intricately designed scales are composed of different materials, unlike the single layer of steel in medieval armor. Moreover, the scales have multiple layers with orientation properties to maximize strength. A closer look at these layers sheds light on why these fish can withstand piranha-infested lakes.

External Layer:

Thickness	600 micrometers
Composition	Made up of a hard, mineralized material

The external layer's surface resembles a wavy texture similar to the corrugated center portion of a cardboard box. The lower valleys of the wave in the scales have slits. This shape provides flexibility to the scale, which is unexpected if you

were constructing a surface impervious to attack. That is, until you consider how it works with the internal layer.

Internal Layer:

Thickness	1,000 micrometers
Composition	Soft collagen fibers

The internal layer is made up of multiple layers of collagen fibers oriented at varying angles with respect to each other. The fibers are long and thin with a strong and weak side. The weak side is the long portion of its cross-sectional area.

It is similar to a plank of wood. It is easy to split wood along its grain, but going against the grain isn't easy. If you have children in martial arts, please know that the spinach you gave them for dinner didn't contribute when they impressively "split" that board in their class. No, it's most likely they were given thin breaking boards with the grain of the wood cut so that it would be parallel to the striking hand.

The opposite is true and observed on the arapaima. Each layer is aligned at different angles to the previous layer, culminating in a stacked structure that exhibits strength in all directions based on the alignment of each layer. What is remarkable is that each layer possesses characteristics of the other layer (in a lower magnitude).

The combination of these scale layers adds its own uniqueness to the overall strength and mobility.

This type of layered multiple material is classified as a composite structure. Together, these layers have been the bio-inspiration at Jacobs School of Engineering at UC San Diego. The result may be a future composite body armor that is both impervious and flexible.

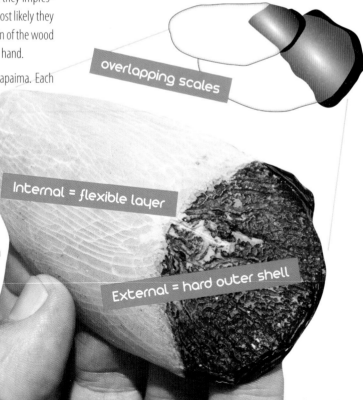

overlapping scales

Internal = flexible layer

External = hard outer shell

A complex dual layer of scales = a composite structure able to withstand piranha-infested waters.

A durable design creates strong "armor" for protection.

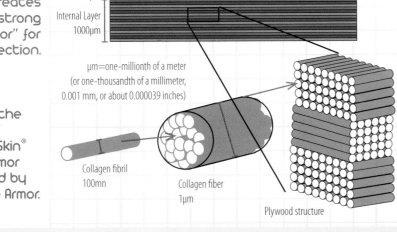

External Layer
600μm

Internal Layer
1000μm

μm=one-millionth of a meter (or one-thousandth of a millimeter, 0.001 mm, or about 0.000039 inches)

Seen in the x-ray of Dragon Skin® body armor designed by Pinnacle Armor.
▽

Collagen fibril
100mn

Collagen fiber
1μm

Plywood structure

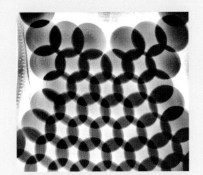

3. STRONGER THAN KEVLAR® — SPIDER–WEB STRONG

It is not only fish being studied for applications related to strength. Spiders are intelligent creatures and have been long studied, admired, and captured in folklore. They have been epitomized in myth, movie, story, and fable. Many hold fond early memories of "Itsy Bitsy Spider" as a favorite children's nursery rhyme. *Charlotte's Web* is a beloved novel from youth, and Spider-man has captivated many an imagination in comics, TV, and movies.

The focal fascination and uniqueness of a spider is inarguably its web. The beautifully intricate interwoven fibers are a marvel to science. The tensile strength of a web is really the stuff of legend. In the world of fibers it is tensile strength that sets one fiber apart from others. Fiber strength is determined when stress is applied, such as pulling from both ends similar to a tug of war. Engineers call this value the ultimate tensile strength, that is, the maximum stress (PSI) that a material can withstand before it breaks.

Every material has a tensile strength, even the seemingly delicate spider silk. Below is an example of comparative metals. The PSI numbers represent the maximum load that the material can handle per square inch. The higher the PSI, the stronger the material is.

Stainless Steel	15-5PH, ½" thick	154,000 PSI
Titanium	Ti-6Al-4V bar, ½" thick	135,000 PSI
Aluminum	7075-T651, ½" thick	75,000 PSI
	SPIDER SILK	253,816 PSI

Spider silk may seem fragile, but the average spider silk is a whopping 253,816 PSI, almost 100,000 PSI stronger than stainless steel.

Okay, so the spider silk has great PSI. But what is the spider silk load equivalent and why do you need to calculate that? Load is one of the characteristics that engineers also use in determining strength to make sure things are strong and don't break easily.

Once we know the ultimate tensile strength of spider silk, we can then determine the actual load (pounds) it can handle by using the following equation:

$$\text{Load (lbs)} = \text{Ultimate Tensile Stress (PSI)} \times \text{Area (square inches)}$$

We can formulate proper models and understanding using both PSI and load numbers to understand in real time the strength of spider silk. As an example, let's assume that we have a strand of spider silk the same diameter as a human hair (.00071 inches, area of hair = .000000396 square inches):

$$\text{Load} = (253,816) \times (0.000000396) = .10 \text{ lbs.}$$

This means that if we were to pull on a strand of spider silk the diameter of a human hair, it would be able to withstand a load of 0.1 pounds before it breaks. If you had 1,000 strands of hair you would need 100 pounds to break the strands. These numbers could make even the strongest of strong men cry.

In terms of available materials to date, only Kevlar® (invented in 1965) had a greater tensile strength. It is commercially produced into things like bulletproof vests. However, it was recently discovered that there is a Malagasy spider with over ten times the toughness of Kevlar®. This recently discovered spider silk is the strongest known biological material to date. With super numbers like that, it is no coincidence that science is trying to invent tougher materials by mimicking the super structure of a spider's web.

Malagasy spider

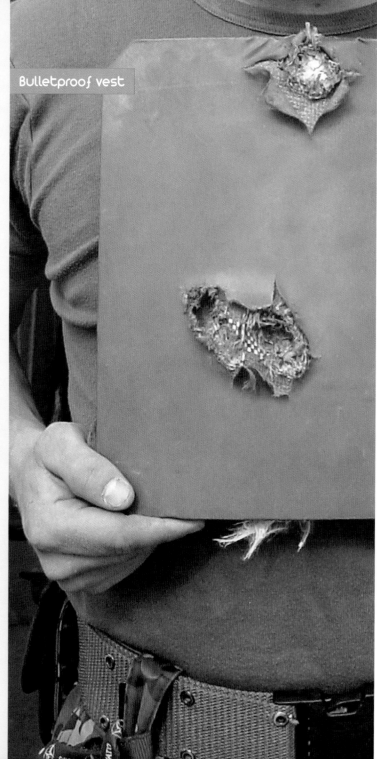

Bulletproof vest

4. PINECONE FASHION COMING SOON TO A MALL NEAR YOU?

I remember looking at this subject as I was writing and wondering if it was a joke. After carefully researching the humble pinecone, I realized that this was indeed a seeming contradiction to the laws of science, which has raised interest in the research of the pinecone (J. Seto).

The quick science is this: We know that as moisture is removed from an object, what proceeds is a physical reduction in overall size. Dehydrated foods are a great example. A grape shrinks when removed of its water content and becomes a raisin. You pack these when you go camping because they take up little space in limited areas like your hiking bag and car.

Not all objects shrink by the same volume. A rock removed of moisture will never turn raisin-like; in fact, we probably wouldn't see much difference in the physical appearance. Can we assume the same would hold true for a pinecone?

The logical conclusion is that when the weather is warm and dry, the scales on the cone would shrink and contract and the pinecone would close. But the opposite is true because of the geometric shape of each of the pinecone scales. A closer look at these scales reveals that each scale is narrow at the base and fans out to a larger blade at the end. The larger blade end has a mass on the lower side, which acts as a counterweight to cause the scale to extend downward.

This is because there is something special lying on the top of the scale. There are two seeds that are waiting to be released when the pinecone opens. Since the seeds are

a different composition relative to the pinecone, the net effect is a difference in the overall shrinkage.

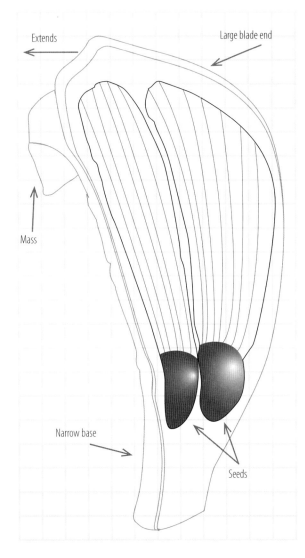

Remember how there is a variance in how different things shrink? Pinecones and their seeds shrink and contract at two different levels. The seeds shrink less than the pinecone and cause more shrinkage to occur at the lower face of the scale as compared to the inner (seed) side of the scale.

Here is how the sequence of this shrinkage works in real time:

1. Dry weather causes moisture to be evaporated from the scale and seeds.

2. The narrow base begins to shrink/contract, in addition to the entire scale and seeds.

3. Due to both the mass on the end and the two different shrinkage amounts, the tip of the scale extends downward, resulting in the opening up of the pinecone to allow the seeds to be dispersed.

The pinecone is one example of a bio-inspired mechanism being copied for smart fabrics. Others include the lotus leaf (water repellent/self-cleaning), algae (UV-protection), and the mimosa plant (touch sensitive).

Relative humidity activates a movement in the structurally functional fabric to help wick away moisture. Changes like this, as a direct result of absorbing or attracting water are called hygroscopic.[2]

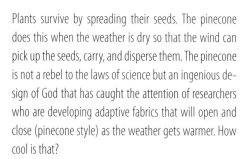

Plants survive by spreading their seeds. The pinecone does this when the weather is dry so that the wind can pick up the seeds, carry, and disperse them. The pinecone is not a rebel to the laws of science but an ingenious design of God that has caught the attention of researchers who are developing adaptive fabrics that will open and close (pinecone style) as the weather gets warmer. How cool is that?

15

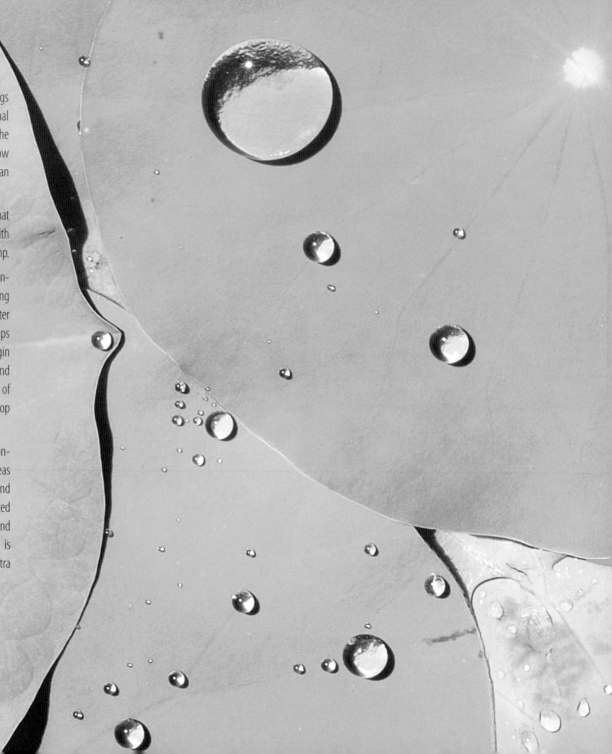

5. CLEANING LIKE A LOTUS LEAF

The natural world we live in offers many beautiful things that seemingly do not offer man any ideas for functional living. Leaves surround us with beauty and we know the function of trees to the air we breathe. But did you know leaves are quite remarkable in the applications they can provide us? The lotus leaf is one such specimen.

The lotus leaf is self-cleaning, thanks to a surface that consists of microscopic bumps. Each bump is covered with nano-scaled tubes that project from the surface of the bump.

As water droplets fall on the lotus leaf, the amount of contact area is balanced by these tubes and bumps. Reducing the amount of contact area causes instability of the water droplet because of the random locations of both the bumps and tubes. The result is that the water droplet will begin to roll along the leaf. This deflects the leaf downward and casts the water droplet off the leaf. The bumpy texture of the leaf with weight of the water drop mitigates the drop toward the unsupported end, thus falling off.

Observation of God's genius in man's naturalistic environment has propelled companies to formulate new ideas based on this nanotechnology of fluid repellency and attraction. This could change the way things are coated to either repel or attract moisture on both organic and nonorganic materials. The potential for self-cleaning is emerging in fields such as clothing and paint, without extra expended energy.

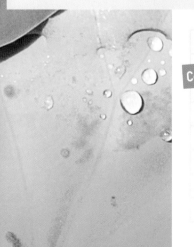

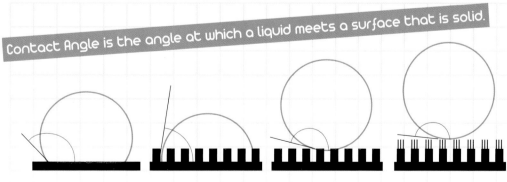

Contact Angle is the angle at which a liquid meets a surface that is solid.

Some plants show contact angles up to 160° and are called super-hydrophobic, meaning that only 2–3% of a drop's surface is in contact. The higher the contact angle the higher the hydrophobicity of a surface.

◁ Water drops (orange) hitting different solid surfaces (black, some with texture, some smooth). Contact angle is shown in gray.

6. ROBOSQUIDS AND JET PROPULSION

Some of God's most amazing designs are found underwater. The squid is one such creature. The elegance and speed at which they can move is captivating and visually hypnotic. Squids have jet engine-like capabilities that engineers would love to replicate. They are fast, effective, efficient, and quiet. Unfortunately, the soft tissue and moving parts of a squid have not made them easy to replicate. But we can study how they move to try to gain knowledge about what makes the squid so quick.

Squid movements resemble pulses, but a closer look reveals the secret behind the squid's propulsion cycle. The squid's head area emits a vortex ring that gives it amazing sprinting speeds of around 20 mph. Squids are torpedo-shaped and, curiously, their heads seem to be located in the back area where the vortex is expelled.

We see vortex rings in jet engines where we see a steady plume of exhaust trailing behind it. But the squid's vortex is a burst of fluid that exits a nozzle and expands in the shape of a donut and then curls back on itself. It resembles a plume, the shape of a donut ring, which gives it thrust and propels it forward.

The rearward-directed thrust that propels it forward is a principle called Newton's Third Law of Motion, which states "For every action, there is an equal and opposite reaction."

This is possible because the main body or mantle of a squid has a cavity that has two openings around its head — an inlet and outlet.

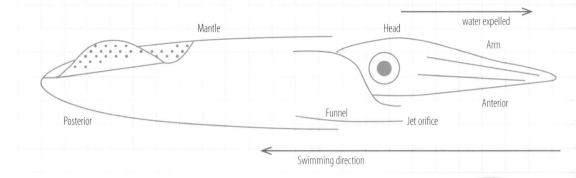

Inlet	the larger opening surrounding the head draws in water and fills the mantle cavity
Outlet	funnel-shaped, which almost looks like an exhaust pipe that expels fluid

There are circular muscles surrounding the mantle that draw in and expel the fluid from its cavity. As the muscles of the mantle expand (open), the squid begins drawing water in from its inlet. Once the cavity has been filled, the inlet closes. The squid then begins to contract its muscles and expels (shoots) out the water through the smaller funnel opening. The funnel is how the squid is propelled at such high speeds and is similar to filling a balloon with air and then letting it go. The force of the air released forcefully shoots the balloon away from you at high speeds.

Southern Methodist University has developed a self-propelled pulsed jet vehicle rightly named "Robosquid." Their dissertation *Propulsive Efficiency of a Biomorphic Pulsed-jet Underwater Vehicle* is axiomatic. The Robosquid aims to construct an efficient, propulsive, underwater vehicle that uses an oscillating piston to generate the pulsed jets of thrust. Their observations could also contribute to those looking toward Nanobots that could be used to navigate through the thick fluids in the human body to diagnose disease.

Technically, it has been challenging to those conducting these studies, but we would not expect any less from studying the complex and wonderful creations of God.

nanobot

NOTE: This nanobot is not to scale. Proposed nanobots are tiny robots that go where others cannot. They vary in size and are typically measured by nanometers. Ten thousand nanometers is about the thickness of a human hair.

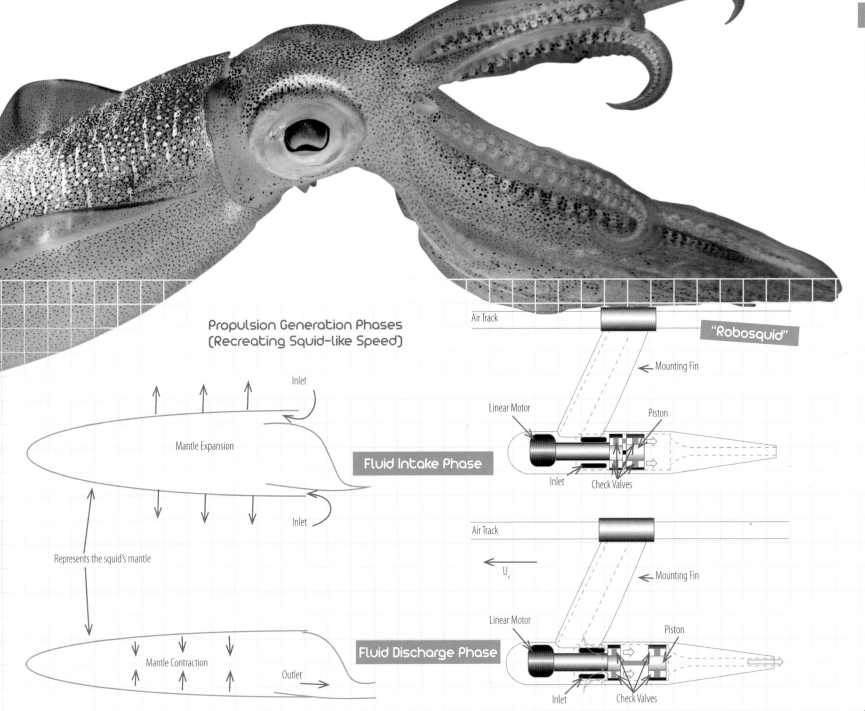

"Robosquid"

Propulsion Generation Phases
(Recreating Squid-like Speed)

Air Track

← Mounting Fin

Linear Motor

Piston

Inlet   Check Valves

Fluid Intake Phase

Inlet

Mantle Expansion

Inlet

Represents the squid's mantle

Air Track

U_v

← Mounting Fin

Linear Motor

Piston

Inlet   Check Valves

Fluid Discharge Phase

Mantle Contraction

Outlet

19

7. MANTIS SHRIMP EYE IMPROVES NEXT WAVE OF ENTERTAINMENT TECHNOLOGY

Technology seems like it's moving at the speed of light. Home entertainment technology has evolved beyond the VCR. What we see and hear matters when it comes to entertainment. We want our reds as red as they can be. We want yellows that make the sun look dim and blues that are bluer than the Pacific Ocean.

Scientists think they may hold the key to the next generation of visual technology after examining the sensitive eyes of a strangely captivating stomatopod known as the mantis shrimp. Biologists have labeled them "shrimp from Mars" because they are biological standouts. The mantis shrimp have intricately complicated eyes that can distinguish between 100,000 colors. That is an incredible ten (10) times more than humans, but their capabilities go

beyond this. They can also see circular polarized light (CPL), an extraordinary ability that no other creature can claim.

Polarization can be illustrated by the glare off another vehicle that you experience when you drive down a sunny road. That glare is the polarization of light after being reflected off the surface of another vehicle. When light hits a reflective surface it will bounce off and be projected onto a two-dimensional plane (flat surface) that is parallel to the reflecting surface.

That glare is the reflection that our eyes see as a blade of light and is known as linear polarization of light. Many sunglasses offer a polarized lens option that filters out polarized light, resulting in a crisp, glare-free image.

The polarization of interest to scientists is circular polarized light (CPL), where light goes through a conversion with a pattern similar to a corkscrew. Data transmitted as CPL allows greater data transmission and lends itself to a loss-free transmission.

Consumers are data-storage hungry. We want more to fit in to less. We want to squeeze more movies, pictures, and information into smaller storage units. It started with CDs and the technology is growing, albeit not at the breakneck speed of other technologies. The CD was first introduced in 1978, DVD in 1995, and Blu-Ray in 2006.

Biologists know the mantis shrimp's eye has the incredible capability of converting linear polarized light to CPLs and vice versa. Remember all those colors it could filter? Mantis shrimp eyes perform this conversion across the whole visible spectrum.

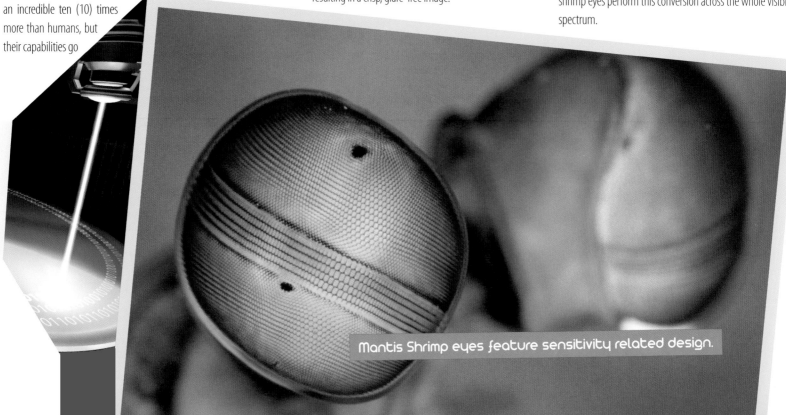

Mantis Shrimp eyes feature sensitivity related design.

Currently the conversion of light is limited to specific colors. They are as follows:

CD/DVD ⇒	Uses red light	wavelength = 650 nanometer
Blu-Ray ⇒	Uses blue light	wavelength = 405 nanometer

Each of these has a conversion that happens for the wavelength of a certain color. The smaller the wavelength, the more data can be stored on a disc. In the numbers for wavelength, bigger isn't better.

Man has replicated this conversion through a Quarter Wave Plate. It converts linearly polarized light to circular polarized light, but only for a few colors of the visible spectrum. This is nowhere near the optical pageantry demonstrated by the mantis shrimp's staggering 100,000-color detection.

Replication of the process through quarter wave plates will change how much data can be stored on optical media (the next Blu-Ray). This will affect the next wave of how we store our entertainment such as our music, videos, and movies. But as a researcher astutely remarked: "The level of structural complexity and precision obtainable through natural self-assembly of biological materials far surpasses any current material manufacturing capabilities."[3]

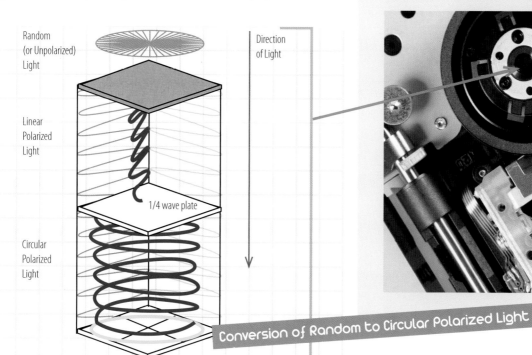

Random (or Unpolarized) Light

Linear Polarized Light

1/4 wave plate

Circular Polarized Light

Direction of Light

Conversion of Random to Circular Polarized Light

8. BUTTERFLIES PREVENT COUNTERFEIT CURRENCY?

There was a saying back in the day that if you were acting crazy men in white coats with butterfly nets would come to take you away. Those men still exist. We call them scientists, and they are using their butterfly nets to catch and study the amazing butterfly. What they have found may further the gadget age, monetary system, and even national security.

These scientists are studying the blue morpho butterfly because of their strong iridescent color. If these properties could be replicated, we would have access to a range of color on bank notes that could make them nearly impossible to counterfeit. Electronic companies have also been researching the morpho butterfly because it could save battery life and increase radio signals. You may be asking: What has hearing (radio signals) to do with visuals (colors)?

Light waves dictate the different colors we see. Each color that we see has its own distinct wavelength; in other words, it has its own frequency. We are more familiar with sound waves like the ones in our car radios. As you rotate the dial you are tuning in to a specific frequency in order to listen to different stations. Each radio station has its own distinct frequency that the wave transmits on.

High   **Low**

A wave is similar to a wave in the ocean with upper peaks and lower valleys. There are big, gentle, slow-moving waves and also small, rapid waves. Visualize the slower waves as low frequency and the rapid waves as high frequency. Color

is seeing the frequency of the wavelength; each color transmits a frequency.

When we see the color blue emanating from a butterfly wing, we are seeing the wavelength (475 nm, nano-meters) or frequency related to the color blue. All other frequencies (colors) are filtered out so that they are not visible.

The wings of the butterfly accomplish a dual purpose:

1. filter unwanted colors from being reflected
2. intensify the reflected color

Structurally, the butterfly wing allows these functions to take place because of the two layers of scales. The scales are one on top of another: the ground layer and the upper layer, which work harmoniously.

Upper layer	a transparent scale layer on top of the ground layer that passes light
Ground layer	the bottom scale layer where light reflects (initially)

It must sound like a game of ping-pong, but this is where the wonder of God's design reveals itself.

Light passes through the upper layer, much like a transparent blind. The light passes to the ground layer, which ricochets the light back through the upper layer. It is this reflection of light back toward the surface that filters out and intensifies a specific color back out and into the eye of the beholder.

The iridescent capability comes from the structural makeup of the upper layer, which is comprised of ridges running the length of the scale. These ridges are not thin, vertical pin-stripes, but have a complex resemblance to a Christmas tree.

This tree structure is finely tuned to filter out all unwanted wavelengths and allow a specific wavelength to pass through. There are relative spaces and thicknesses between each layer that will allow only a specific wavelength size to pass through. Complexity at such a microscopic nano scale is improbable without the Master Designer, God.

In a nutshell, wavelengths interfere with other wavelengths. If they occur at the same time, they are In Phase, which means brighter and brighter color moving up on this tree structure on the ridges of their scales. If they don't occur at the same time with other waves, they are Out of Phase. This can cause them to cancel each other out and never reach the top of the tree.

Governments are interested in incorporating this knowledge toward bank notes, where replicating the colors cannot be achieved through normal pigment applications. Companies are using the reflection technique to create incredibly sharp computer displays.

As God has allowed us to see things on a nano scale it has opened up avenues for technology on a precise, microscopic scale. Better gadgets, money that can't be counterfeited, and virtually tamper-proof identification cards. Men in white, get out your butterfly nets!

The iridescence of the wing is altered when submerged in water. The result is a seemingly radical change in color.

Canada and other countries are introducing polymer bills using reflective technology. Although not as complex as the morpho butterfly, it is a step in using color to deter counterfeiting.

9. HUMAN EYE — A BETTER CAMERA LENS

We often take our eyes for granted, but they are the lenses through which we view the world. The human eye is a marvel to science. It is uniquely wired, intricately complicated, and has been long studied for replication. It would be fair to say it's been eyed with interest by digital camera makers.

The hemispherical shape of the eye surface area adds additional exposed area as compared to a flat surface. This spherical shape is the most effective shape for a wider field of view. The transfer of microelectronic components onto a curved surface without breakage is a challenge, but it's worth investigating.

It's been established that a certain shape gives the widest field of view. But what is transpiring behind this frontal surface tells us how and why this works. As light travels through the front of the eye, the image is projected onto millions of photoreceptors called rods and cones. These are attached to the rear surface (retina) of the eye. The retina is also hemispherical in shape, this providing the most efficient placement of photoreceptors and unparalleled image resolution. The image is then converted to electrical signals and gets sent to the brain for processing.

Hemispherical-shaped surface to hemispherical retina equals effective processing of images. Perhaps that's oversimplifying it a bit. But in order for cameras to effectively process images and provide the best field of view, the following need to exist simultaneously:

1. Proper location

2. Shape of the photo detectors (sensors)

3. Installation on a hemispherical surface

We must not forget about the photo detectors that would need to replicate the placement of the rods and cones in the eye. Researchers knew this would be a challenge. Currently, camera sensors are fabricated in a two-dimensional planar surface arrangement. This is because any flexing of the sensor package would cause damage, due to the brittleness of the sensor material.

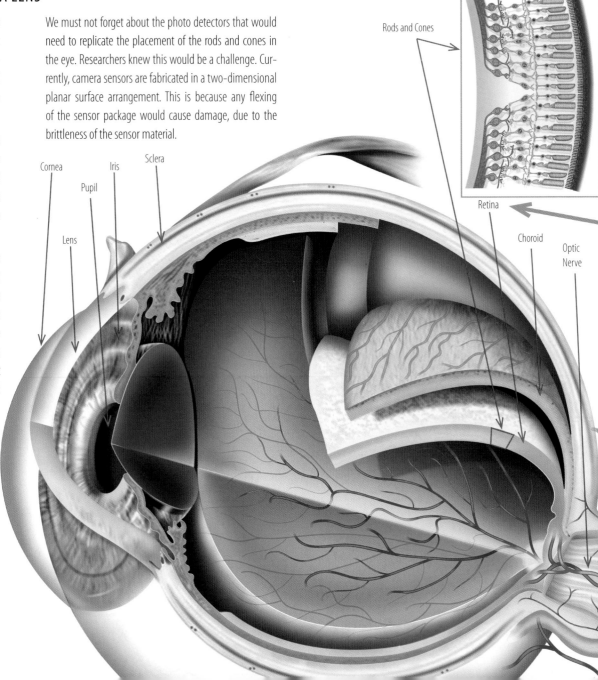

Rods and Cones

Cornea

Iris

Sclera

Pupil

Lens

Retina

Choroid

Optic Nerve

Sensor Array

Engineers have come up with a very clever solution to mimic a curved surface sensor package. It begins with fabricating a square segmented sensor array pattern with each sensor joined at each edge by a looped segment, to allow flexure of the sensor package over a curved surface. The looped segments provide the required stress relief when the array is formed to a hemispherical shape.

The replication of the retina surface has been the most efficient method for maximizing a camera's field of view. Engineers have fabricated a sensor array capable of 256 photo detectors. This pales in comparison to the human eye's millions of photo detectors. It is a step in the right direction, albeit a small step.

Solomon understood this when he proclaimed in Proverbs: "The hearing ear and the seeing eye, the Lord has made them both" (Proverbs 20:12).

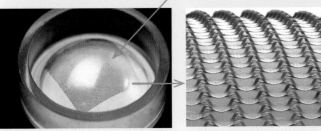

10. COMPUTER VIRUS SOFTWARE LOOKS TO HUMAN IMMUNE SYSTEM

Anyone who has ever had a computer virus knows the frustration of losing all your files, your pictures, everything you stored on your computer in a split second. Anti-virus software has long existed, but the number of new viruses that can affect your computer is increasing at an alarming rate. A computer virus is similar to a virus that can affect the human body. What better place to look for a solution than to investigate how the body attacks a virus? Scientists are analyzing the human immune system to determine if this is a realistic goal.

The main source of defense for current antivirus programs is through the use of a virus dictionary. This is a snapshot in time of known viruses that have been identified. It helps fully adapt antivirus programs to detect, isolate, and kill viruses, protecting your computer. Can these programs be as smart as the human immune system? Let's first look at what scientists are trying to emulate.

We are "fearfully and wonderfully made" (Psalm 139:14). Anyone who has peered into a microscope to look at a cell cannot help but be impressed by what is revealed. The immune system is a galaxy of complex organisms that work harmoniously and efficiently. The ingenuity and complexity revealed as we study how the body operates engenders awe.

Scientists are looking at creative programs modeled from this network of protection in our immune system to protect our computers from viruses that can disable them. No one knows for sure how many computer viruses exist, but we know the number is high and growing at a rapid pace. The current antivirus systems available fall woefully short in combatting these new viruses. The antivirus software that is available is programmed like a virus dictionary where known viruses are catalogued. However, this is similar to looking for a crime suspect who has no known record; you won't find them in the database because they've never been recorded.

What scientists envision is a creative program that will detect, attack, destroy, and protect. But is it really that easy? How much time and computing power will be required if it operates on the same computational level as our immune system? These problems must be solved by scientists before they can move forward. First things first: What is the human immune system?

Just as with any potential computer antiviral system, the first line of defense is that it has to be quick to react. Our body's immune system leaps into action when invaded by antigens (foreign substances). Even a simple sneeze is your body's means of expelling a foreign substance.

The main lines of defense are white blood cells or leukocytes, which come in two basic groups: lymphocytes and phagocytes. I like to think of lymphocytes as the strategists and phagocytes as the soldiers. They are kind of like the brain and brawn, scattered throughout our body and working in concert with each other to guard our bodies from disease and infection. They also create their own special defense against future attacks — the antibody.

STRATEGIST ➔ Lymphocytes

Antibodies are cells that remember the antigens, in case they decide to attack again and help destroy them — the strategist guarding against future attacks. They latch on to specific antigens and produce antibodies (proteins), which

Scanning Electron Microscope (SEM) Image of an Antibody

continue to reside in the body to guard against any future occurrences.

SOLDIER ➔ Phagocytes

These are cells that attack and destroy the antigens. Acting immediately, they latch on with the lymphocytes to destroy.

The body has 20 amino acids that can be configured to create either a peptide or antibody (both are proteins). A string of 100 or more amino acids of the 20 that are available is an antibody. Any fewer than that constitutes a peptide.

Back to the attack on the immune system: Once the antigen has been attacked by white blood cells, it leaves behind the antibodies that guard against future attacks (the protein created from the lymphocytes).

This is the creative protective program of the human immune system that is being studied in order to come up with ways to protect our computers from viruses. But if scientists and computer programmers were to create algorithms that mimic the creation of antibodies, they have a mathematical mountain in front of them. The numbers are simply stacked against them.

Remember how we looked at those 20 amino acids that create peptides and antibodies? These amino acids can be shuffled in any combination, even the same amino acid a few times or multiple times! The combinations are staggering if we look at the peptide with its 20 amino acids.

The numbers look like this for peptides: Out of the 20 amino acids there are 20^{20} combinations, which equates to 1.05×10^{26} (or presented in a familiar format: 105,000, 000,000,000,000,000,000,000). You can imagine how long it would take to generate all of these combinations. We'd have to factor how fast computers can run the program and then see how much time it would take. Roughly, it looks like this: computer speed per second x seconds available in a year = combination per year calculated.

Computer Speed	We have to make a primary assumption that the scientist's computers can effectively run one million combinations per second.
Seconds Per Year	We break down the time to figure out how long that might take. One year equals 60 seconds per minute x 60 minutes per hour x 24 hours per day x 365 days per year, which equals 31,536,000 seconds in one year.
After One Year	Combinations = 31,536,000,000,000 for the peptide

Is that it? No, that is only the combinations of one single year. How about all the combinations that are mathematically possible? How many years would that take?

It would take 3,325,000,000,000 years to run all the combinations for a peptide, which contains 20 amino acids. It would be mind-numbing to imagine if it were an antibody, which can contain a chain of close to 30,000 amino acids strung together, as compared to this little peptide with only 20.

Optimistically, it seems quite improbable to accomplish given the mathematical odds. I realize that is a seemingly contradictory statement, but that does remind us of our opening thoughts on this issue.

"I praise You, for I am fearfully and wonderfully made; marvelous are Your works, and that my soul knows very well" (Psalm 139:14). This helps us take on a new and humble reflection of who we are and who God is.

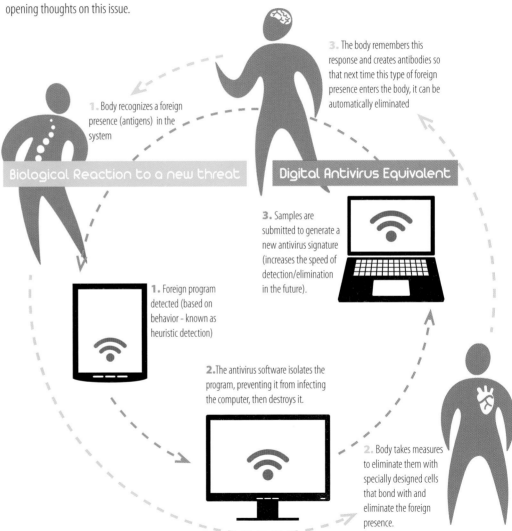

Biological Reaction to a new threat

1. Body recognizes a foreign presence (antigens) in the system

2. Body takes measures to eliminate them with specially designed cells that bond with and eliminate the foreign presence.

3. The body remembers this response and creates antibodies so that next time this type of foreign presence enters the body, it can be automatically eliminated

Digital Antivirus Equivalent

1. Foreign program detected (based on behavior - known as heuristic detection)

2. The antivirus software isolates the program, preventing it from infecting the computer, then destroys it.

3. Samples are submitted to generate a new antivirus signature (increases the speed of detection/elimination in the future).

11. THE HUMAN BRAIN INSPIRES FASTER COMPUTER CHIPS

One of the most creative monster movies in black-and-white was the Frankenstein movie. It goes something like this: Dr. Frankenstein proceeds to construct a being from body parts of deceased humans. The doctor goes further; he implants an abnormal human brain in the creature and it came alive. It is creepy and hair-raising as it becomes an evil monster with intelligence.

We know that this movie would not have been possible without the human brain. The human brain is being studied for improvements for computer processes. It is frighteningly complex — it is staggering to think of the intricacy. The functionality of the brain is controlled through the transmission of electrochemical signals from one neuron to the next. The brain consists of approximately 100 billon (100,000,000,000) neurons (nerve cells) and transmits the electrochemical signals among the neurons through gaps between them called synapses.

The number of synapses is not a one-to-one ratio with respect to the number of neurons. There are approximately 100 trillion (100,000,000,000,000) synapses between these neurons. When information needs to be transmitted, the data is essentially flung from one neuron to the next. This is called synaptic transmission.

Any one neuron is connected to between 5,000 and 200,000 neurons. The amount of data flowing between neurons is so large that it is greater than the number of stars in the universe.

The basic anatomy of a neuron consists of the cell body (or soma) considered to be the control center. Attached to the cell body are the structures that act as conduits for data coming in and out of the nucleus. Incoming data flow through the dendrites, and outgoing data flow along the axon. As outgoing data reaches the end of the axon (termed axon terminal), the data is then transmitted across the synapse to the adjacent neuron dendrite arm through a process called synaptic transmission.

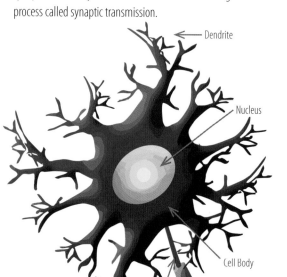

Dendrite

Nucleus

Cell Body

Myelin Sheath

Axon

Axon Terminals

Any one neuron is connected to between 5,000 and 200,000 neurons.

There are as many as 10,000 specific neurons in the brain, categorized into three groups:

1	Motor neurons (conveys motor information)
2	Sensory neurons (conveys sensory information)
3	Interneurons (conveys information between different types of neurons)

Scientists have been trying to understand and copy the human brain's ability to communicate through neurons. Attempts have been made to replicate the functioning properties of a single neuron. Researchers at MIT have designed a computer chip comprised of about 400 transistors to replicate the transmission between two neurons across the synapse.

These ambitions don't stop at just replicating a single synaptic transmission, but include complete neural functions, such as the visual processing systems. Let's crunch the numbers to see if this is feasible (not taking into account the system operability).

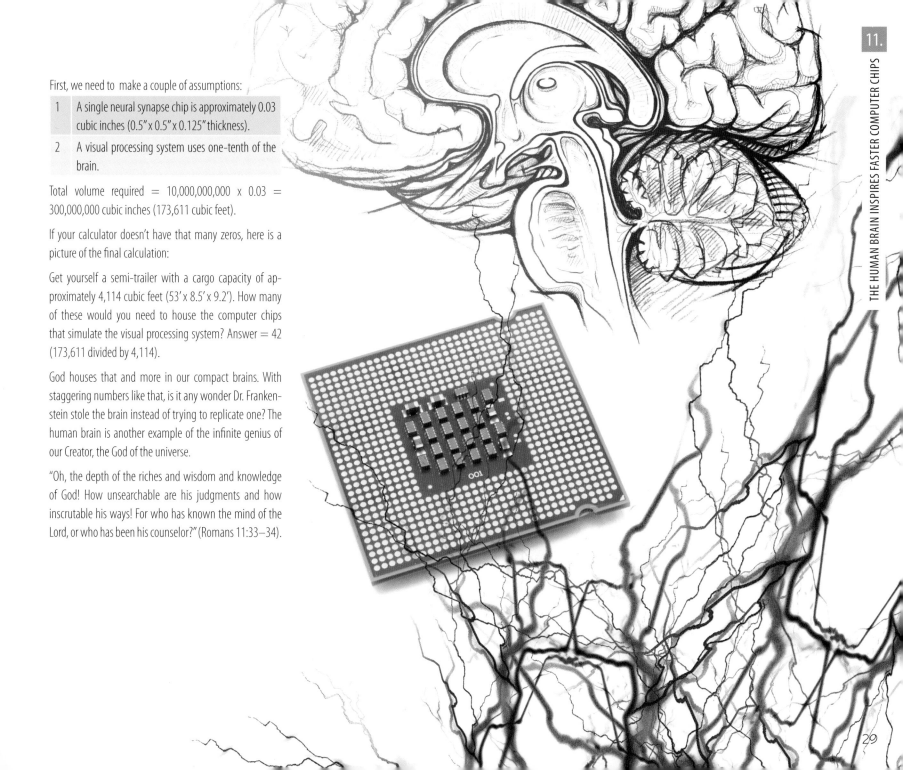

First, we need to make a couple of assumptions:

1. A single neural synapse chip is approximately 0.03 cubic inches (0.5" x 0.5" x 0.125" thickness).

2. A visual processing system uses one-tenth of the brain.

Total volume required = 10,000,000,000 x 0.03 = 300,000,000 cubic inches (173,611 cubic feet).

If your calculator doesn't have that many zeros, here is a picture of the final calculation:

Get yourself a semi-trailer with a cargo capacity of approximately 4,114 cubic feet (53' x 8.5' x 9.2'). How many of these would you need to house the computer chips that simulate the visual processing system? Answer = 42 (173,611 divided by 4,114).

God houses that and more in our compact brains. With staggering numbers like that, is it any wonder Dr. Frankenstein stole the brain instead of trying to replicate one? The human brain is another example of the infinite genius of our Creator, the God of the universe.

"Oh, the depth of the riches and wisdom and knowledge of God! How unsearchable are his judgments and how inscrutable his ways! For who has known the mind of the Lord, or who has been his counselor?" (Romans 11:33–34).

12. ANTI-LASERS LEARN FROM BIRD FEATHERS

You don't have to look far to see the diversity of nature. You can look right outside your door to see a variety of shapes, colors, and geometry that can inspire the pen to poem and song. Birds exemplify the creativity that God possesses. We are irresistibly attracted by their sweet song, elegant movements, and vivid, radiant palette. We see illusions of Picasso or Crayola painting broad strokes of sharp color on regal costumes that adorn our aviary friends. But a closer look reveals the nano secret of these brilliant colors.

It all begins with light. After all, we couldn't see any color without light. Although it seems like a contradiction: even white light has color. It isn't white but is an array of colors ranging from reds to violets. It's best illustrated when you shine light through a prism and see the dispersion of light into each of its color components. The color characteristic is determined by its wavelength, the physical length to the color. Each color has a wavelength. Blue, for example, has a wavelength equal to 475 nm (nanometer).

Bluebirds and blue Jays obtain the colors in their feather not from pigments but from spherical air pockets trapped within their barbs. The size of the trapped air is tuned to the wavelength of a set color. As light passes through the sphere, it scatters and the end result is a color that will not fade over time and looks absolutely brilliant.

How could this phenomenon be recreated in the lab? You could shine a light on a flat plate with different sized holes to scatter the wavelengths. The resulting colors would be dependent on the size of the wavelength color and perforated holes. Both would work in perfect symphony to manipulate the color you wanted transmitted.

This is what Yale physicist Hui Cao and her colleagues set out to do. According to *Wired* Magazine, Hui Cao said, "After we learned this, we said, 'Oh, that's a smart idea!' "[4] Her team created a 190-nanometer-thin sheet of gallium arsenide (a special semi–conductor that transmits light efficiently) with holes drilled in it spaced between 235 and 275 nanometers apart. When the team lit up the wafer, it produced a laser light with a wavelength of around 1,000 nanometers.

It replicated the color-producing nanostructures within the feathers of a bird to scatter light at specific wavelengths. The colors were determined by the short range order of the spacing between the air pockets in the feathers. Cao and her team realized that by changing the spacing in between the holes they were able to change the wavelength of the laser. Cao said, "We can have control, and it doesn't have to be perfect. That's what we learned from nature."

The research turned into a quest to improve laser efficiency using a short-range order to enhance light confinement. It was a new two-dimensional mirror-less laser and was coined the first "anti-laser." A smart idea? A good idea? More like a God idea.

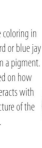

The blue coloring in a bluebird or blue jay isn't from a pigment. It is based on how light interacts with the structure of the feathers.

The ability to manipulate color displays, developed from the way colors are displayed when light hits the feathers of a bird, has future applications. Light enters a sheet with dimples and holes in a specific pattern and this pattern creates specific colors for the viewer. Scientist can alter the holes in the sheet to change the colors that are displayed.

13. DECODING THE BOMBARDIER BEETLE

The bombardier beetle is an enigmatic creature. This insect can wage chemical warfare by rapidly firing off a spray of boiling, noxious liquid when it senses danger. Cursory studies of the individual components as well as the system architecture that constitute the beetle's infrastructure of blended fluids, combustion, and nozzle control reveal the system requirements of a superior biological, physiological, and engineering phenomenon.

The complexity of the engineering requirements is reflected in this brief spec sheet below:

Bombardier Beetle System Requirements

Design intent	Defense system
Armament	Toxic benzoquinone
Temperature	100°C (212°F)
Range	10 times the length of unit
Primary ingredients	Hydroquinone, hydrogen peroxide
Active ingredient	Oxidative enzymes
Reservoir	1 - storage of primary ingredients
Combustion	Chemical
Discharge activation controlling parameter	Pressure
Discharge nozzle quantity	2
Nozzle sweep	360 degrees
Discharge rate	500 pulses per second

There is enough work here to keep many, many engineers busy (and frustrated) for a very long time. The first design layouts would undoubtedly focus on the main design goal of engineering a system similar to the beetle's spray mechanism. This fluid delivery system would be capable of firing off toxic vapors at a rate of 500 pulses per second at a temperature equal to the boiling temperature of water — 100°C. It must also be directionally controlled from each of the exit nozzles.

Fortunately, we don't have to brainstorm a way to achieve these system requirements. God has already taken care of all the details for us in the bombardier beetle as a prototype. Engineers must then employ their skills to deconstruct and comprehend the mechanisms involved and how they interact with each other. A good place to start is to use the bombardier beetle and its spray sequence as our blueprint.

Gland that produces hydroquinones and hydrogen peroxide

Reservoir

Valve

Combustion Chamber

Discharge Nozzles

Glands that produce special catalyst enzymes

Bombardier Beetle Spray Sequence:

1. Preparing	The bombardier beetle uses two primary chemicals for its spray warfare: hydroquinone and hydrogen peroxide. These are produced in glands and stored in a reservoir in a mixed state. The reservoir has an outlet valve that opens and closes to the combustion chamber. As the valve opens, a small quantity of the mixed fluids fills the combustion chamber. The valve closes when the combustion chamber is full.
2. Mixing	Like a mad scientist's chambers, the setting is the lining of the combustion chamber that releases oxidative enzymes. These enzymes cause a chemical reaction with the mixed fluid. The result is a transformation into a toxic fluid called benzoquinone and raises the fluid temperature to boiling.
3. Firing	Once the fluid reaches the boiling point, pressure builds up within the combustion chamber, causing the two discharge nozzles to open. The fluid is both at a boiling temperature and under pressure as it leaves the nozzles. Instantly it vaporizes as it discharges to a lower pressure region (referred to as flash vaporization), and the deadly toxic concoction is discharged like a cannon. This complete cycle is then repeated another 499 times, all within a time span of one second. That is 500 times in one second in a revolvable and oscillating trajectory.

The bombardier's defense system has been likened to a hybrid of tear gas being shot out of a tommy gun; it is chemical warfare dispensed with the deadly precision and force of an assault rifle. All of this is without harm to the beetle. The potential applications include a new generation of efficient devices. An aircraft that has lost engine power could reignite instantly. Drug-delivery devices such as inhalers could be far more reliable. Fire extinguishers could dispense both fine mist and large droplets of water from the same canister.

The bombardier beetle's firing system was copied by researchers at Leeds University, England, though not at the same discharge rate. Leeds' researchers were able to heat up water to boiling and discharge it at a rate of 10 to 20 cycles per second. Instead of a chemical reaction that causes the temperature to rise in the chamber, the researchers used electricity to heat the water. They were inspired by the beetle's control valve system and built upon the physiology of the beetle's ability to generate rapid vapor explosions. Their platform technology is licensed to a Swedish biometrics company and named the µMist® spray system.

The bombardier beetle's unique defense system could inspire improvements in engine ignition systems and drug delivery devices.

14. MOSQUITOS STUDIED FOR PAINLESS NEEDLES

Is there anything better than a summer night? The air is warm and the smell of barbeque is wafting in the air. It's simply perfect . . . until you realize that a mosquito has bitten you. More specifically, a female mosquito, since they are the ones that do the biting.

Why is it you never feel the bite but you'd as soon faint when your doctor draws blood? Attempts to mimic a mosquito bite have great implications for people who must use needles regularly, such as diabetics or those who rely on medicines that can only be administered through needles.

The pain of the insertion of a needle depends on three things. Minimizing these will hold the key to decreasing the pain associated with needles:

1	Skin nerves contact area
2	Penetration force
3	Angle of penetration

It is not by stealth that the mosquito manages to bite you and leave without being swatted. The secret is the intricate way in which their proboscis (stinger) works, harmonizing all three of the above.

Micro engineers in Japan have been studying the stinger of the mosquito. This stinger is actually a nose called a proboscis that resembles on a microscopic level the trunk of an elephant. This elongated and tubular appendage is a straw-like mouth, which is the sucking mouthpart of the mosquito.

The proboscis is the tubular mouthpart that the mosquito inserts to draw blood for the proteins it requires. It's a three-part sandwich-type assembly consisting of

- two outer maxilla (outer sheath)
- a center tubular labrum (draw tube to siphon the blood).

Now that we know the equipment, let's observe how it works.

1 Skin nerves contact area

What is unexpected is that the maxilla (outer sheath) is jagged in texture. It doesn't resemble a needle but does resemble a serrated steak knife. The mosquito's proboscis is highly serrated, unlike conventional sleek needles. Jagged edges mean that only small points come in contact with the skin. This reduces the stimulation of the nerves, which reduces pain because the contact surface is minute compared to a smooth, long needle that makes a great deal of contact with the skin. But how does the mosquito use its jagged-edge maxilla to penetrate without being immediately squashed?

2 Penetration force

What makes this assembly unique is the method it uses to penetrate the skin and also reduce skin nerve contact. Instead of a straight push down to break the skin, the mosquito vibrates the proboscis at a rate of approximately 15 Hz (i.e., 15 cycles per second). The vibration helps achieve the penetration depth required yet reduces the amount of force required as compared to a straight push.

The proboscis is like a jackhammer, which vibrates up and down with its spade, penetrating the concrete to break it up. At the end of each cycle, the spade penetrates with a little more force and goes a little deeper until the concrete breaks.

3 Angle of Penetration

The final phase of a mosquito bite is the angle of penetration it follows. It is scientifically superior.

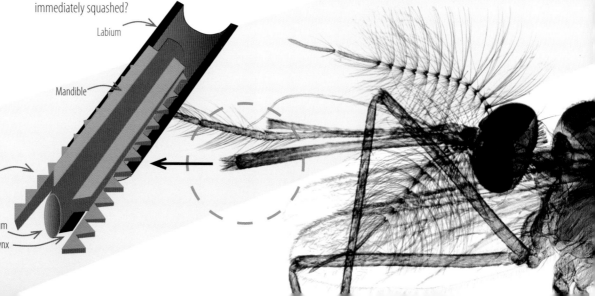

Labium

Mandible

Maxilla

Labrum

Pharynx

You would think that all this jackhammer-like shaking of jagged-edge needles would result in a very obvious mosquito bite as it begins sinking its needle into your tender flesh. After all, the nerves in the skin are triggered whenever anything comes in contact with them.

The penetration area is dependent on the angle at which the needle is inserted. The area of penetration would be a circle for a vertically oriented needle. The area becomes decidedly more elliptical when the needle is slanted at an angle. This slanted configuration gives a larger area and the pressure felt is now much lower because of the reduced penetration pressure on the skin.

Summary: Less pain. What a wonderful thought — a world where medicines administered through needles are more comfortable to the patient.

15. LISTEN LIKE A FLY ON A WALL

Sound waves fill our lives with inexpressible joy. Although we can't see them, we would be unable to hear the sweet sounds of birds, ocean waves, beautiful music, or children's laughter without them. But how can something we can't see help us to hear?

Sound waves propagate by pushing the air that comes in contact with your eardrum at a varying intensity and frequency. Your eardrum is a diaphragm (think of it as a small piece of paper). It vibrates based on the sound pressure waves' intensity and frequency, which results in the range of sounds audible to the hearing ear. What you get is sound, but where did that sound originate?

The ear feels the effects of the sound waves. If sound comes from the left side, your left eardrum will sense a higher pressure and intensity than the right eardrum. This results in a differential variance between your left and right ears. Right now our brain has to do the math to figure things out.

Here is an example of what that might look like. Let's say the left ear hears 10 dB (decibels) and the right ear hears 5 dB of sound pressure. Let's look at this as a simple math equation.

What we come up with is 5 dB more sound coming into the left ear. This is just one example. There is an infinite amount of variables the brain may be called on to calculate for sound and to evaluate where that sound might be coming from. Inefficient, no, but it does take time, like when you hear an emergency siren but cannot pinpoint exactly which direction it is coming from.

But the *Ormia ochracea* fly is configured to instantly pin point where sounds are coming from. Their left and right ears are spaced closer and are attached at the center to a circular disk, creating a structural link. Zero gap. The sound pressure waves it hears from the left and right ear are summed up immediately at the circular disk. This circular disk does the math and tells the brain the difference in sound pressure levels, which is highly efficient. The ormia detects direction of sound far more precisely since it's ears are joined, in contrast to our humble human ears.

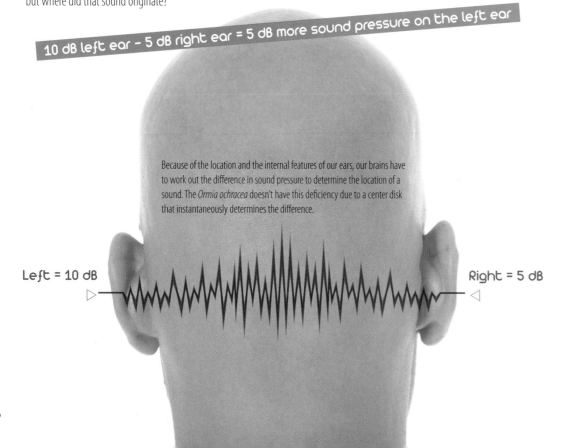

10 dB left ear – 5 dB right ear = 5 dB more sound pressure on the left ear

Because of the location and the internal features of our ears, our brains have to work out the difference in sound pressure to determine the location of a sound. The *Ormia ochracea* doesn't have this deficiency due to a center disk that instantaneously determines the difference.

Left = 10 dB

Right = 5 dB

But exactly how is this being applied in modern science and technology? Patent No.: US 7,146,014 B2. This is a current patent, which replicates the ormia fly's ear system. Yes, you read correctly; it is a patent on a fly's ear. What an incredible example of observing something as insignificant as a fly to patenting one incredible sound system that is intricate and complex in design. It could one day benefit those not as blessed with the sounds that we enjoy every day which we take for granted and with which our lives would be greatly diminished.

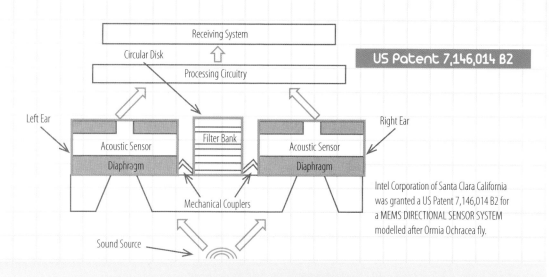

US Patent 7,146,014 B2

Intel Corporation of Santa Clara California was granted a US Patent 7,146,014 B2 for a MEMS DIRECTIONAL SENSOR SYSTEM modelled after Ormia Ochracea fly.

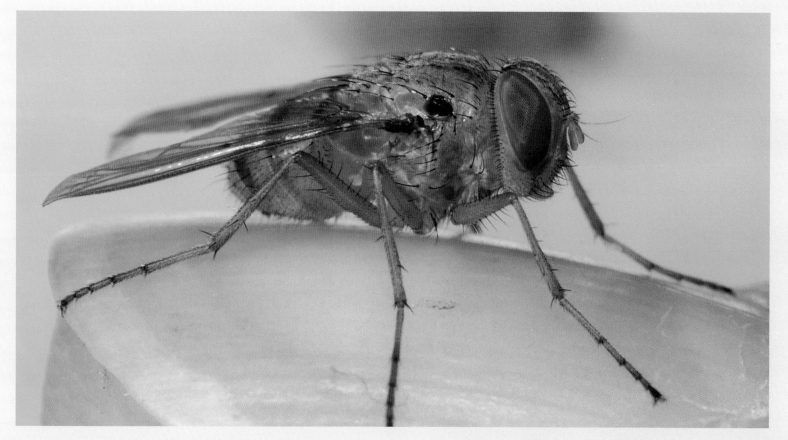

16. HEALING POWER OF THE BODY INSPIRES SELF-HEALING MATERIALS

Scientists are really working overtime to get a glimpse of how to do what God has already done. The imagination of these scientists has branched into such fields as molecular biology, nanotechnology, and quantum mechanics. Nowhere is this seen more clearly than in the medical realm. It has even crossed over to a relatively new field called materials science, which blends science and engineering with matter toward the inception of newer, stronger materials.

Studying the natural world and importing that into man-made matter has been aided in quantum leaps by the microscope. The discovery of the microscope has given a glimpse of fresh new ways of approaching materials engineering.

A method of self-healing, (repairing materials by impregnating plastic capsules with a healing agent within a structure if impaired) has been proposed by researchers at the University of Illinois and published in the *Journal of the Royal Society Interface*. Since we know that only living matter can heal itself, this method would appear to be an irreconcilable proposal. Human flesh that is cut can heal itself, but the process is not a simple progression. You have broken capillary blood vessels located beneath your skin, which cause blood to rush to that area. The first line of defense is to stop the flow of blood and seal up the broken blood vessel. Fortunately, you already have the sealant present within your blood.

Scientists have been toying with the idea of creating a network of self-healing properties that will lie dormant until activated by a break in the material. The biggest challenge to these scientists is to provide a network of paths to transport the healing sealant to any location. This poses a challenge because the more network paths present in a structure, the weaker the structure becomes.

But how is it that the human body can do exactly that? When the surface of our skin is breached, the healing function of our body goes into action. And that network is considerable. These breach detectors are blood vessels and capillaries residing just below the skin's surface and are thousands of miles long (approximately 100,000 in an adult body).

Any disruptions to the blood vessels are quickly aided by the clumping up of blood platelets. We have three major types of blood cells — red, white, and platelets. Platelets are the smallest and take up the minutest fraction of the total blood volume. Since they are the lightest of the three cells, they are pushed to the walls of the blood vessels as blood flows.

The fascinating fact is that the initial response to a break causes the platelets to take on a different form. They have proteins on the outside (similar to muscle proteins) that have the ability to change their shapes — that is, to grow in all directions. They stick to both the break in the blood vessel and to each other, and provide the clumping ability.

As the proteins begin to coalesce, they change to a round shape with filaments extending from them. Each cell continues to change its shape and they become attached to each other as they start to form a network. Like a football huddle, they all gather in to a tight unit. The density of the platelets begins to increase and begins forming a plug to the broken vessel, stopping the blood from leaving your body and foreign matter from entering.

It is exactly this cycle of blood circulation that inspired researchers at the University of Illinois to conceive of an engineered healing agent through a man-made micro-vascular healing system network. However, it has a severe limitation. Any breach of the system network that lies outside of its coverage will not receive any of the healing agent.

Man is uniquely and inarguably the most complex of God's marvelous creations and is only now being appreciated at a nanostructure level.

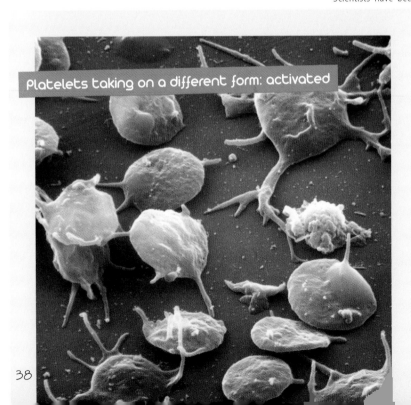

Platelets taking on a different form: activated

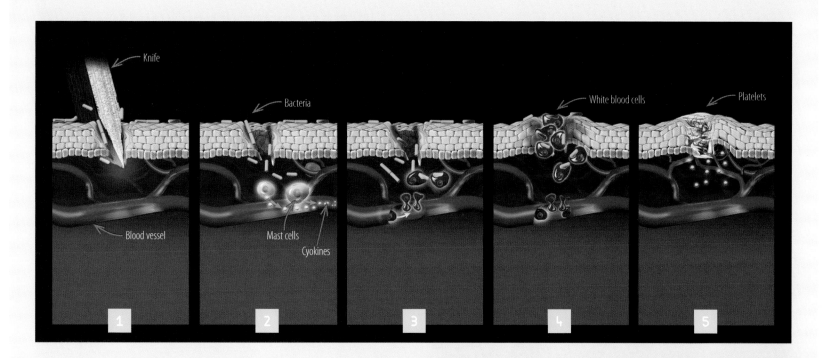

Knife

Bacteria

White blood cells

Platelets

Blood vessel

Mast cells

Cyokines

1   2   3   4   5

1   Bacteria enter through a skin wound caused by a knife.

2   Bacteria enter the wound, causing an infection. Mast cells detect the bacteria and release cyokines (signaling chemicals) into the blood stream, which attract other immune cells.

3 & 4   White blood cells (macrophages) migrate to the site of the infection and engulf the bacteria (phagocytose).

5   Hormones stimulate the production of wound-healing materials, such as platelets and fibrin.

A healing agent contained in a microvascular network helps a polymer repair its own cracks. Credit: Janet Sinn-Hanlon, Univ. Ill.

self-healing plastic

39

17. HUMANS GIVE ROBOTIC DESIGN A HAND

Some of the things coming out of labs and engineering offices these days are the stuff of science fiction meets fairy tale. The narrative reads like a robot that comes to life because it is so human.

Scientists have been experimenting with robotics for decades, with great gains in the field of prosthetics. However, it isn't simply a matter of copying the shape of a hand or arm. The skin's sensing capabilities and ability to send signals to our brain to execute a command demands precision in range of direction and force of touch, as well as working in unison with the other fingers, wrist, etc., to complete a task.

The human hand, however, cannot be improved upon even with modern-day science wizardry. The robots that are created have designs that are similar to the human hand but nowhere near as intricately created.

Four fingers and an opposable thumb may seem mundane, but the precision it takes to pick up a dime or tie a knot truly show the ingenuity of God. Those who have played sports and have sprained or broken a finger understand how a simple thing like writing a note can become quite the task!

The first thing your hand does before it takes any action is to sense what it is doing. The nerves in your skin provide a feedback loop to your brain to determine the course of action that will be taken. Will it pinch, sweep, flip, clutch, or do some other motion? These mechanical contrivances of the hand would appear to be technically challenging. However, how you sense what you are touching is the trickiest part.

We apply pressure whenever we touch an object. The amount of pressure will vary based on what we are touching or grabbing hold of. Something delicate will require light pressure. If you really want to get a good hold on something heavy, you will apply greater pressure.

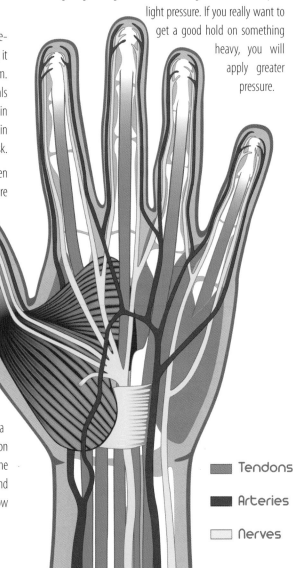

Tendons

Arteries

Nerves

Pressure is the measurement of the amount of force applied per square inch of area or PSI (pounds per square inch). Pressure sensors convert a physical force into an electrical signal output that corresponds to the applied pressure. This conversion works through what is called a Wheatstone bridge electrical circuit, known in electrical engineering circles simply as a Wheatstone bridge.

The Wheatstone bridge consists of four interconnected arms. Each arm represents an electrical resistance. Whenever there is a resistance change in any of the arms, the Wheatstone bridge produces an electrical output. The resistance change is accomplished through a strain gage. A strain gage is composed of minute filaments that loop back and forth, creating a grid pattern. The strain gage gets bonded to the surface in question, and when the surface is deflected or when pressure is applied to the surface, the grid pattern in the strain gage stretches. This stretching of the grid pattern causes a change in resistance in the strain gage. When there is a resistance change there is a corresponding Wheatstone bridge output, which correlates to the pressure applied.

Through the Wheatstone bridge circuit we are able to determine the magnitude of the pressure that the skin is experiencing by converting the mechanical pressure input to a corresponding electrical output.

Forming a basis of understanding of the mechanics of the human hand communicating with the brain has advanced the future of prosthetics by leaps and bounds. This will enable those who have lost limbs the advantage of a better quality of life in things that many of us take for granted, such as running or catching a baseball.

Industrial robotic grippers differ greatly from the construction of a five-fingered robotic hand. The aim is to duplicate the complex sensory mechanisms of the human hand to adapt its dexterity for the task at hand. Researchers are developing the world's first real-sized prototype using the human hand as its model.

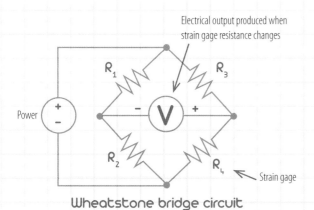

Electrical output produced when strain gage resistance changes

Power

R_1 R_3

R_2 R_4

Strain gage

Wheatstone bridge circuit

One arm of the bridge is the strain gage (R_4), while the remaining three arms (R_1, R_2, R_3) are resistors that remain constant.

Conversion of Mechanical Pressure to Electrical Output

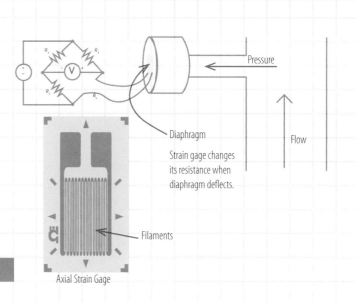

Pressure

Diaphragm

Strain gage changes its resistance when diaphragm deflects.

Flow

Filaments

Axial Strain Gage

18. MUSSELS WITH STRONG MUSCLE-STICKING POWER

The affordable and abundant mussel has been called the poor man's oyster. If you've cooked them at home then you know the cleaning routine. Rinse, scrub, and rip off the stringy beards to throw in the trash, then toss them in the pot for dinner. Anyone who has cleaned mussels can attest to the force that must be exerted to rip the beards from the mussel before cooking. This adhesive strength did not escape the notice of researchers funded by the U.S. Department of Energy.

Examination of the strands of the beards reveals that a circular foot is attached to the tip of each strand. The foot anchors to any hard surface, whereby the mussels shore themselves to resist pounding waves and surging tidal basins.

Mussels are typically found clumped together in groups, attached to each other and the ground by their beards, also known as byssal threads. At the end of these threads is a sticky adhesive plaque. What is fascinating is that the thread and plaque are formed in a matter of minutes and are the key to their strength and survival.

In short, the tandem process requires the following:

1. The ability of the foot to bond itself to any surface in water
2. The composition and creation of the byssal threads and plaques

Initially, the mussel uses its thin, tongue-shaped foot as a feeler. It extends outward from its shell to locate a suitable surface to attach itself to, and grabs hold with just the tip of its foot. The foot begins to contract to rid the cavity of any water.

The complicated manufacturing process begins from a deep groove running the length of its foot, very similar to a cement truck chute. Proteins are secreted down the foot and left to harden. Some researchers say up to 11 proteins exist, but to date only 5 have been found and are identified as:

MFP-1, MFP-2, etc., where MFP = Mussel Foot Protein.

The whole process only takes about two to five minutes, and what remains is the newly created byssal thread and plaque firmly attached to the surface. Byssal threads do not crack and have a knobby appearance which structural scientists theorize that it might lend to its tensile strength properties.

An adhesive with strong holding power up to 1,000 psi that can bind to natural surfaces like wood and rock, as well as fabricated ones like plastic and nonstick Teflon, do not exist outside of the mussel.

Adhesives are a billion–dollar industry and demand for them is growing. A mussel-adhering glue that is super strong and can be applied underwater while maintaining strength would be revolutionary.

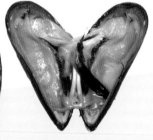

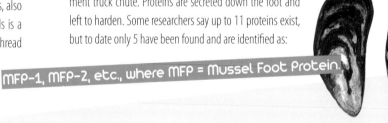

Foot extends and attaches to surface

Proteins secreted into groove of foot

Foot is removed, newly created byssal thread and plaque

Process repeated

Start

Mussel Attachment Sequence

Finish

The practical applications are limitless. Usage would expand outside conventional adhesion to include aqueous environments, as well as difficult and specialty adhesive applications.

Perhaps the most exciting potential is as a biomedical adhesive with promise in the surgical, dentistry, ophthalmic, and orthopedic fields. Best of all, it would be safe for human and animal applications. It would be biocompatible, nontoxic and environmentally friendly. It's no wonder there are patent applications for the few mussel proteins researchers have identified in the quest for the last glue you'll ever need.

No wonder scientists have been trying to replicate the mussel's ability to adhere to any type of surface. The foot of the mussel can attach to any surface, even the slippery surface of Teflon. Coupled with the byssal threads that yield high tensile strength, it's certainly understandable why scientists have been studying for decades what God has given the mussel the ability to do in two to five minutes.

19. VELCRO® IMAGINED IN THE WOODS, REIMAGINED IN THE LAB

Many think of the fields of biomimicry and biomimetics as relatively new fields of science. These are terms to describe the transfer of ideas and inspiration from the fields of biology to technology by using observable nature to inspire new designs and improve or provide sustainable solutions.

Would you be surprised to find that the principles behind these new fields have existed for quite some time? Many of the best inventions have arisen from those who studied God's creation because it works and is engineered brilliantly. There is an infinite study that could be made and we would still never plumb the depths of God's genius. We aren't even in the shallows.

A Swiss engineer named Georges de Mestral was walking in the woods with his dog and made one such unexpected discovery in the 1940s. Fresh from his walk, he noticed that he and his dog were covered in burrs. Our first instinct when foreign matter attaches itself to our clothing is to remove it by brushing it off. This won't work with something like a burr.

Burrs are spiky-looking seeds of dry fruit. Upon returning home, de Mestral inexplicably plucked off a burr and took it to his microscope. He curiously observed a long hook on the end of the burr. The purpose of the burr's long hook is to latch on to something like loops in clothing or animal fur in order to disperse its seeds far and wide. The proper name for this method of attachment is hook and loop, and it is very effective.

This so intrigued de Mestral that he began conceiving of a fastener employing these principles of hook and loop, and he later invented Velcro®. I'm sure many of us have not thought of Velcro® as a hook-and-loop system but that is exactly what is. One side is a piece of material filled with a very densely packed sea of loops while the other side is an ordered sequence of hooks arranged in a fine grid pattern.

The grip of this new invention would be ideal if every hook was engaged with a loop. This would provide maximum joint effectiveness and even load distribution. The more hook and loop combinations that are engaged, the better the loading coverage and potential to handle more loads and not detach.

It's similar to hanging a sheet on a clothesline. If you use only two clothespins, one on each end, you will notice the sheet sagging in the middle. What if you added 20 pins? More pins equals less sag with each new pin. Velcro is the same in that more hooks and loops equals better load coverage.

Velcro's® ability to disengage the hook-and-loop combinations after it has been engaged contributed to its success. Through experimentation, de Mestral decided nylon was the best material for the repeated fastening and unfastening durability of Velcro®. Nylon deflects and returns to its original shape; this is what is referred to as elastic behavior.

Today, Velcro® is ubiquitous in everyday life. It can be found in shoes, watches, hair curlers, and the list goes on and on. It is so effective that even NASA has used it on space shuttle missions. But the story of Velcro® isn't over. Velcro® has progressed beyond nylon to plastic, steel, and even molecular structures.

Currently, German engineers have taken the hook-and-loop concept and designed a piece of Velcro® able to support a 35-ton load. Their material of choice for the Velcro was 0.2 – millimeter–thick steel.

Velcro® is progressing past natural materials like nylon and steel and looking toward the nano world. Researchers are trying to develop nano versions of Velcro® that are molecular structures to do entanglements that would be two hooks instead of hooks and loops, and that may be as strong as epoxy yet removable. There is ambitious research for a blood-clotting agent that can control bleeding and be removed without causing further damage. Velcro® is indeed astonishing and evolving in ways that may change the medical landscape.

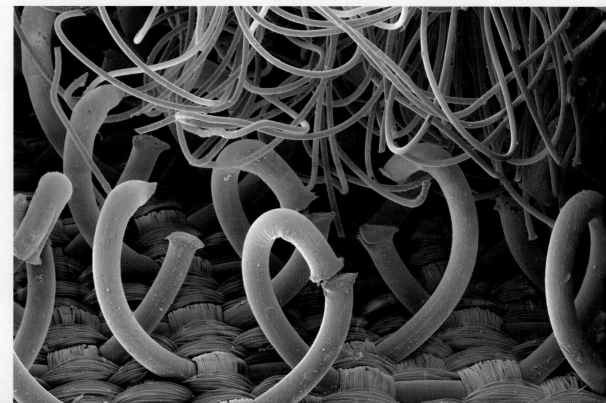

20. WASP NESTS AND PAPERMAKING

In the beginning was the Word, and the Word was with God, and the Word was God (John 1:1).

Where would those sweet words be without paper for all to read? How would we fulfill the Great Commission without the printed words of life from our Bibles today? Fortunately, none of us have to imagine that. Previously, words were recorded on materials like papyrus, parchment, cloth, and even animal skins. The process was laborious, time consuming, and potentially costly.

Paper as we know it was first recorded to have been invented in China in A.D. 105. It was a well-guarded secret for about 500 years. Eventually, different countries dabbled in making paper. It was not as we know it today, but a laborious task that included pulping and baking materials.

Printing had been around since Gutenberg invented the printing press, but it was pulped paper that made printing a commercial success, opening it up to the masses. Yet even today our best efforts at papermaking cannot compare to the paper wasp.

In the 1700s someone observed wasps chewing up wood, spitting it out pulped before forming nests. René-Antoine Réaumur was a chemist and naturalist. He watched wasps making paper nests from wood, that were built to last. He reasoned that if paper wasps could chew up and pulp out paper for their nests, perhaps he could follow a similar process. His research contributed to the pulping techniques of the mid-19th century for the process of papermaking we have today.

Although we now have a complex and efficient way to produce paper, the core of what Réaumur observed is strikingly similar to today's technique. It's not your mom's recipe, but it is the basic formula currently used for making paper used in newspaper, books, stationery, boxes, etc., that takes its methodology in theory from Réaumur who observed the wasps making their paper nests.

Wasp Nest Making Recipe:

1   Chunk some wood from a tree.

2   Chew the wood, breaking it down into tiny fibers.

3   Add saliva, which contains proteins to help bond the fibers together.

4   Lay out the pulp from mouth to existing surfaces. As time passes, the newly laid out pulp begins to harden and forms the desired shape it was laid out in.

5   Voilà — a new nest.

The key here is to break down the wood fibers. The finer the fibers the more structurally sound the paper will be at the end.

Even with all of our knowledge today, our paper isn't as durable or well-constructed as the paper wasp's. But we are farther along than would be without Réaumur's observation of these little creatures.

Modern Papermaking:

1   Break down the wood to its fiber level. This is done by breaking down pieces of wood as small as possible (ideally as fine as shavings or dust).

2   Add fluid to bond the wood fibers together. Add water to the broken-down fibers. Allow wood fibers to absorb the water and begin clumping and adhering together.

3   Allow drying time for the bonding of the fibers to take place. The pulp is then flattened and pressed flat. Excess water is extracted during the drying cycle.

4   Voilà —today's paper (e.g., newspapers, books, school notebooks).

21. CAT EYES THAT SAVE LIVES

The copying of God's design can have life-saving benefits. We owe one such copied design to God's plan of a cat's eye. The optics of our feline friends are truly amazing, and their shimmering eyes in the dark have been frequently observed. The reflection of the feline eye caught the eye of one Percy Shaw from the United Kingdom who invented and patented his design in1993, calling it Catseye™.

Catseye™ is the name given to road reflectors on streets, which you have no doubt seen if you have driven a road at night where there is insufficient lighting. Catseye™ are weather resistant and amazingly useful on foggy days, when it would be otherwise perilous to drive.

Some objects can appear to glow when you shine light on them. This occurs for several reasons:

1	Reflection of the light
2	Refraction/absorption of the light
3	A combination of both

Light coming in must also go out for a reflector to work efficiently, and that only happens when the angle of the light coming in is greater than the critical angle. This occurs when the angle of refraction is equal to 90 degrees. Any refracted angle above 90 degrees will result in total reflection of the light source.

Man and also many animals have a special reflective layer called tapetum lucidum in their eyes. The physical shape of the tapetum lucidum helps achieve this total reflection. A sphere is the ideal shape, as a tapetum lucidum layer functions like a mirror in the back of our eyes. This can sometimes cause the red eye in your photos when the camera flashes — the light is bouncing back.

Low profile Catseye™ road studs

Reflective spheres shown set into a Catseye™ in the United Kingdom

The satellite dish has also utilized reflection technology. Their parabolic shape utilizes their centroid (center) as RF (radio frequency) waves hitting the curved surface reflect and propagate toward the centroid. No matter where the RF waves hit the curved surface, it will always reflect toward the centroid, which is an inherent property of parabolic surfaces. The waves bounce back, which is why satellite dishes were created curved in shape.

The design that reflectors have in common is that they consist of hemispherical reflecting surfaces with the mating half consisting of a clear lens. The light coming in to the reflector bounces off the rear spherical surface and is projected back out the clear lens. This concept of light reflecting back out the same way it came in is referred to as retroreflection.

This is the reason we can see the reflectors on the roads; the light is bouncing back to us. It kind of makes me wonder if that's why I can never win in the carnival toss game? Hmm...

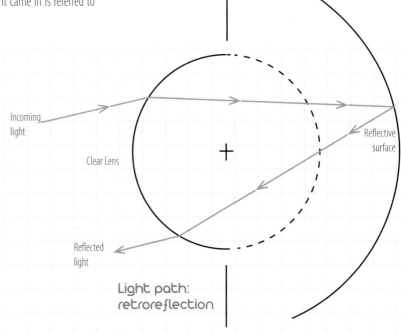

Incoming light

Reflective surface

Clear Lens

Reflected light

Light path: retroreflection

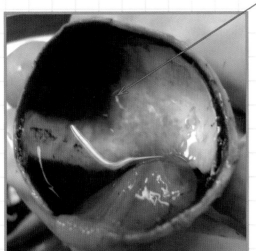

Tapetum lucidum membrane

The dissection of a calf's eye was done at the University of Pennsylvania. It shows the retina (pinkish gray) loosened from the back of the eye, hanging down. Revealed is the tapetum lucidum (opalescent turquoise). You can see the reflective pigment layer that gives the shining appearance to eyes when they are illuminated in the dark.

49

22. GECKO FEET HELP ROBOTS GO VERTICAL

Stickybot™ sounds like the new toy craze for kids, but it's actually the invention of Mark Cukosky, a professor of mechanical engineering at Stanford University. Stickybot™ is a robot that can climb smooth surfaces and was inspired by the intricate design of a gecko's toes.

Gecko toes are utterly fascinating on the microscopic level. The chemistry makeup and many components of their toes lend to their incredible adhering and detaching properties, which could only have been designed by God.

To begin, each toe has hairs, which are called setae. Each hair then branches off further to hundreds of tips called spatula. These spatulas are what come in contact with the surface while the gecko walks. There are millions of spatulas working to get the gecko where it wants to go.

The adhesion properties are so effective because there are attractive forces (electromagnetism) between molecules (i.e., the molecules of the spatula and the contact surface). When we talk about this type of attraction we are referring to a charged state.

Any molecule can be in one of three states:

1	positive
2	negative
3	neutral

We all learned this in science class at one time or another with magnets. Here's a quick refresher: As a general guideline, any charges that are of the same polarity will repel each other. For example, if you were to put two positive charge molecules next to each other, they would repel from each other. Conversely, if you were to put a positive and negative charge beside each other, they would attract, seemingly pulling toward each other. The old adage is true: opposites attract. The neutral charge has neither a negative nor positive charge and is considered a zero charge. It will neither repel nor attract a positive or negative charge.

All magnets have both a positive and negative side. If you take two magnets and align each one so that the positive sides face each other, you will find it rather difficult to put the magnets together. However, if you align them with the positive and negative sides facing each other, you will find it difficult to keep them apart.

This is the principle in play, and the gecko's spatulas produce small forces as they come in contact with a surface. These small forces are referred to as Van Der Waals forces. The spatulas are extremely tiny, but when we consider the overall quantity to be in the millions, they collectively produce a very large force.

Stickybot™ could lead to robots that can easily scale vertical surfaces to access hard or dangerous places. They could even lead to adhesives for humans. This is the stuff that comic books are made of.

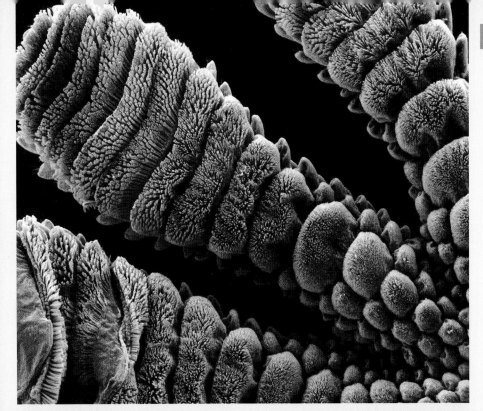

Clockwise from top left: Stickybot™; microscopic close-up of a gecko foot; Stickybot's™ foot; millions of hairs on each ridge of a gecko's foot.

23. WHY FISH ARE FASTER

It makes sense that man would look to marine life to mimic marine vessels. The flow of a dolphin in water is amazing to behold, and its smooth, softly rounded shape unlocks the mystery — an advantage that also applies when traveling through air. The general rule is the more blunt (dull) an object is, the slower it will move.

Blunt = slower
Smooth = faster

We can increase speed by studying the streamlines around the dolphin's body. Streamlines are used as a speed gauge for a traveling object. They are fluid flow lines that travel adjacent to an object and represent the fluid flow velocity around the object. The smoother the flow is around a body, the faster it will travel. Laminar flow is smooth flow. The engineer will pick a shape that results in an abundance of laminar flow when speed is the goal.

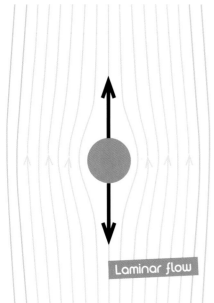

Laminar flow

A round ball results in smoother flow than a square block because the rounded edges smooth out the flow around the ball. Marine life has a variety of such shapes, sizes, and functions in the natural world.

There is a negative in this flow equation called turbulent flow that we want to avoid because erratic flow characteristics slow things down. This is also known as drag.

Killer whales are built for speed with their sleek, rounded shape. Their forms are closely replicated in the shapes of submarines for speed and efficiency. We see it in all kinds of useful applications today such as airplanes and submarines. You see it also with speed skaters and professional bicyclists and their smooth, tapered helmets. Thank you to our friends of the sea!

turbulent flow

Streamlining technology in action mimic's that of the killer whale for sub design (previous page), and bike safety helmets (top); avoiding turbulent flow (center) increases speed and efficiency for a variety of applications, including airplanes (bottom).

24. FINS FOR FANS

At first glance, the bumpy fin of the humpback whale isn't exactly where one might look to improve efficiency for wind speed in fans and turbines. The whale's bumps, known as tubercles, do not exactly fit the current models of smooth, swift, razor-like blades spinning through the air, but that's exactly what they do in the sea. The humpback whale's elegance as it slices through air while breaching or lunging seems almost impossible considering their weight and length.

One of the most important fundamental qualities in aerodynamics is smooth airflow. The smoother the airflow over a surface, the less drag or resistance occurs. The tubercles on the leading edge of the fin create individual passageways for the water to flow between them. What results is smoother flow, and when more tubercles are present, the smoother flow appears along a longer span of the fin.

Picture a garden rake you drag through the sand. Smooth grooves are left behind in the sand by each of the teeth of the rake. This same principle occurs when the fin of the whale is pushed through water. What remains is smoother water flow left behind by the fin. Smoother flow along the length of the fin results in larger rotation angles resulting in greater efficiency.

Angles also play a part in improving airflow. Think of the humpback whale bumps as fingers. What happens when you put your hand outside of the car window?

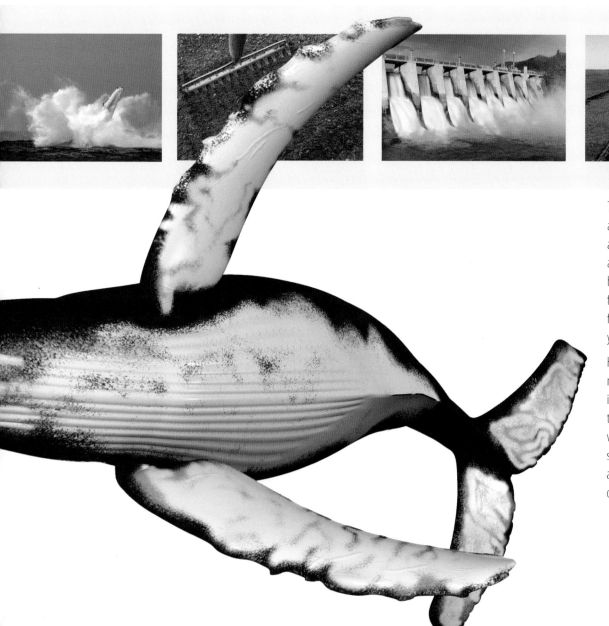

That would depend on the positioning of your fingers and their angle. Let's say your fingers are tightly snug against each other, creating a flat surface with your hand and your fingers facing forward. If you start with your hand horizontal and slowly rotate your hand with your fingertips moving upward, what happens? You begin to feel pressure on the bottom of your hand, wanting to lift your hand up and away.

However, if you slowly spread your fingers apart, you feel more pressure on your hand. What you feel is a reduction in the pressure on your fingers, which gives you the ability to rotate it at higher angles. The bumps in a humpback whale are similar to your fingers spread apart. This seemingly paradoxical design by God has the ability to affect new and innovative products by those who have observed and want to replicate it.

25. TERMITES AND AIR-CONDITIONED BUILDINGS

My parents knew a time without air conditioning, and the home we grew up in did not have that luxury. I hate to confess this, but as an adult who has lived in different parts of the world, I can't imagine living in a place that didn't have air conditioning!

It might come as a shock to find out that a mall in Harare, Zimbabwe, was built in 1996 without air conditioning. Keeping a building cool without any mechanical controls may seem daunting, but the inspiration was the strange termite mounds in the Zimbabwean Savannah. Understanding how termites build their mounds for airflow and coolness inspired architect Mike Pearce to build Eastgate Center Mall (pictured below) with a completely unique design.

Here's how airflow breaks down. As it moves in one door (point A) then leaves through another door (point B), it contains a constant physical property called "mass flow." Mass flow is essentially the weight of air traveling per a given time period. Put another way, it is how many pounds of air you can move in a second between point A and point B.

In our observation here, it is what happens between these two doors that causes air to move. If we look at the two areas in the design of the termite mound we will see the important part it plays in moving the air. Termites build their mounds with airflow in mind. The colony would die if the temperatures outside their mound varied outside the range of 35°F (2°C) and 88°F (31°C).

Their solution is architectural:

1. The shape of the tunnel, which is tapered in sections — referred to as a venturi

2. The location of the inlet and outlet of the tunnel. The inlet is at a lower elevation than the outlet (which is located on the top area).

To properly understand this we must address each physical feature individually as to the cause/effect on the airflow circulation.

Shape of the tunnels

There is a fundamental geometric element in the tapering section of these tunnels, with a smaller area at the base and the larger area located on the top. The smaller area of the tunnel is called the throat and the larger one is called the exhaust. The geometric differences between these two areas are what causes the air to flow.

This is a scientific principle called the conservation of mass ($Rho_1 \times A_1 \times V_1 = Rho_2 \times A_2 \times V_2$). Put very simply, what goes in must come out. This is measured by mass flow, which is the principle we are observing in these termite tunnels.

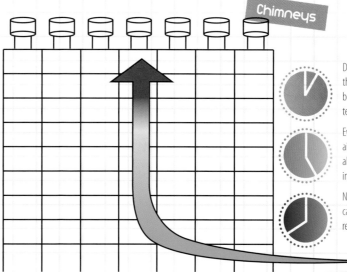

Chimneys

Air moving through a building designed without air conditioning

Passive cooling works by storing heat in the day and venting it at night as temperatures drop.

During day: machines and people generate heat, and the sun shines. Heat is absorbed by the fabric of the building, which has a high heat capacity, so that the temperature inside increases but not greatly.

Evening: temperatures outside drop. The warm internal air is vented through chimneys, assisted by fans but also rising naturally because it is less dense, and drawing in denser cool air at the bottom of the building.

Night: this process continues, cold air flowing through cavities in the floor slabs until the building's fabric has reached the ideal temperature to start the next day.

Start of day: the building is cool.

The big picture is that the mass flow going into the throat will equal the mass flow leaving the exhaust. But further examination of the throat reveals the faster air movement. Conversely, in the area of the exhaust (which is much larger than the throat) we observe slower air movement.

To summarize: As we look back at the tunnel, we notice the base (the throat) has faster-moving air as compared to the air on top at the exhaust. The end result is airflow from the inlet to the outlet.

Location of the inlets & outlets

Location, location, location. Never is that more true than when we look at the locations of the inlet and the outlet of these termite tunnels. One might think that the termites would need a fan to keep the airflow moving. It's not as if they are in areas where there is a constant breeze — so exactly how does it work?

The principle in play here is the standard atmosphere table — as we increase in altitude the pressure around us decreases.

Higher altitude = lower pressure

Lower altitude = higher pressure

Keep that in mind as we now go back to location (where the inlet is located). Here's where it all works together. The inlet is at a lower elevation — a higher pressure. The outlet is at a higher elevation — a lower pressure. Objects move from a higher pressure to a lower pressure. What happens when you blow crumbs along your dinner table? The crumbs move away from your mouth (higher pressure) and move toward the other end of the table (lower pressure).

The combination of these physical properties produces an inherent flow that is constantly moving between both the high-rise building and a termite mound.

Termites do it with little more than clay or sand, saliva, and wood. The Eastgate Mall needs a little help from fans to keep air flowing, but the structural principle came from studying the termite mounds. It has been touted as a rare case of architectural bionics — the field where living organisms are transferred into engineering.

Portcullis House in London uses cooling technologies similar to termite nests (close-up, middle; exterior, at right).

26. BROKEN BONES, HEALING, AND THE EIFFEL TOWER

Have you ever had anyone tell you to break a leg? That is a paradoxical statement when you want to wish someone good luck, but if you know anyone who has ever had a broken leg, it is neither good nor lucky. Do you realize that it is actually very difficult to break a leg? It's much harder than you think.

God's design of the human leg is a feat of structural engineering. Bone is lightweight when we factor it proportionally to its load strength. Surprisingly, when you dissect a bone you find that it is not one whole piece but is comprised of tiny open pockets, all intersecting and resting on one another. Architects and various disciplines of engineering have copied this structural model.

Pre-Industrial Revolution structures like the Eiffel Tower and Statue of Liberty were considered risky because of their unconventional height and shape, with trusses and arches that seemed unlikely to withstand strong gusts of wind. The truss structure was a new feat in civil engineering. Trusses are triangular units and connected at joints like you see in the Eiffel Tower or many bridges.

Structural engineering deals with load paths and load distributions. Any structure that does not move is said to be in static equilibrium. In simple terms, that means that all forces exerted on the structure and all forces that the structure itself exerts balance each other out. It's similar to a tug of war — the push/pull concept that one side must equal the other side to achieve static equilibrium.

When you set your cup of coffee on the table in the morning you will notice that the cup is not moving. Suppose the weight of the cup exerts a downward force of two pounds on the table. The table is supporting the cup, but for the cup to remain stationary the table must exert an upward force of two pounds on the cup, or you will have a spilled cup of coffee.

$\triangledown$ Cup = 2 lb. downward force

$\triangle$ Table = 2 lb. upward force

= Static Equilibrium

This example is a great illustration of how truss structures work by self-reacting. The adjacent members help balance out the loads from each other across each joint. The key with truss structures is the strength-to-weight ratio. Trusses solve the dilemma of building a structure that is too heavy and balance it out with trusses so that engineers can build bigger and higher while keeping static equilibrium. Trusses create many open pockets in a structure, but still have the capability of creating a load-balanced system, quite similar to the human bone with its many open pockets.

God's design of the human leg is a feat of structural engineering.

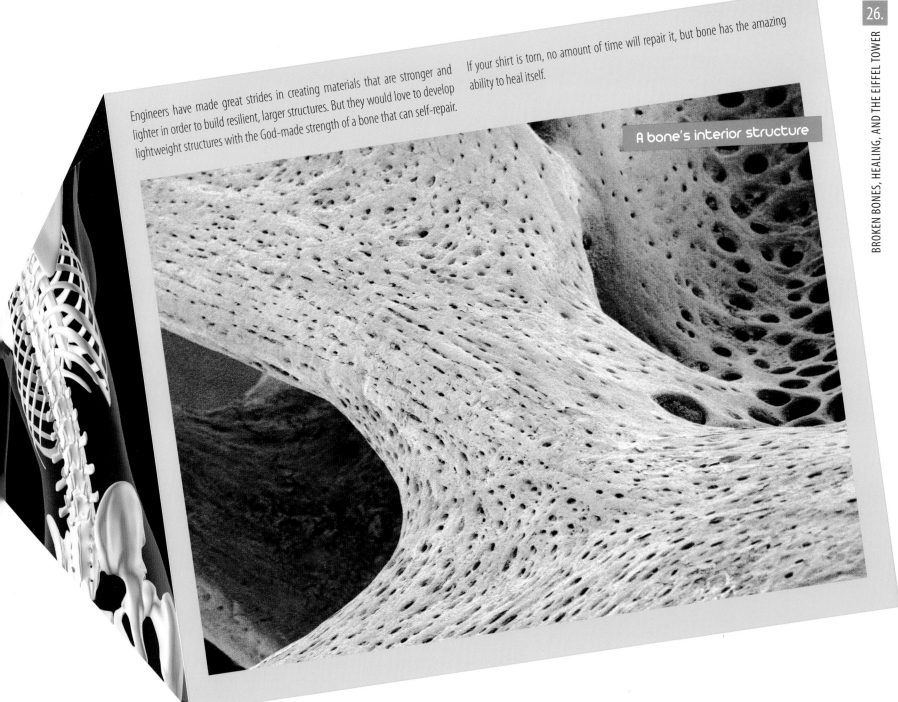

Engineers have made great strides in creating materials that are stronger and lighter in order to build resilient, larger structures. But they would love to develop lightweight structures with the God-made strength of a bone that can self-repair.

If your shirt is torn, no amount of time will repair it, but bone has the amazing ability to heal itself.

A bone's interior structure

27. WIPERS, EYES, AND CONTROVERSY

Some stories seem destined for the movies. In 2008, Hollywood did a biographical story on mechanical engineer Bob Kearns for the movie *Flash of Genius*. Kearns' story was perhaps too colorful to be made for the movies but his was a story with the dramatic human components of a modern-day David and Goliath. Kearns' flash of genius was conceiving of windshield wipers that would blink like an eye. We call them intermittent wipers.

Most of us have cars that have several intermittent wiper speeds. In the 1950s there were only two speeds — on and off. According to Kearns, an errant champagne cork struck his left eye on his wedding night, which permanently damaged his vision. He would tell others later that he couldn't see clearly when driving through rain with his 1950s incessant wipers and impaired vision.

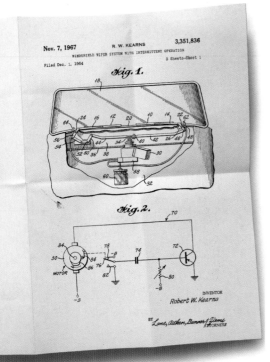

That was the moment Kearns wondered why there couldn't be a windshield wiper that worked like an eyelid, blinking occasionally. He was a mechanical engineer who loved to tinker in his basement, and he began modeling a mechanism that blinked every few seconds.

Could it be that Kearns observed that the blinking of an eye sufficiently lubricates it and prevents it from drying out? Fluid is drawn up from the approximately 30 tear ducts at the edge of each eyelid. Perhaps he noticed that eyes blink in unison to clear out contaminants that blur vision. It would seem that he recognized that eyelids close and open with different speeds: slow, medium, and fast.

Bob Kearns invented an electronic variable timer circuit that would provide power to the wiper motor in intervals. The wiper speed could be adjusted through a potentiometer (variable resistor). He pitched his idea to the automakers and demonstrated the functionality of his design, but he didn't get a licensing deal from any of them. In 1969, automakers began offering intermittent wipers as optional equipment even though Kearns received his patent two years earlier.

This was the beginning of many lawsuits and court battles. Kearns took on the auto industry's Big Three, whom he thought stole his idea. He represented himself, and it was a case of the little guy going up against the giants. Almost 30 years later, in 1995, it went all the way up to the U.S. Supreme Court.

Kearns did win almost $30 million in settlements from Ford and Chrysler eventually, but not before his battle took a toll on everyone, including his family. He spent more than $10 million in legal fees and was said to have suffered from physical and emotional breakdowns. His family supported him, but unfortunately his marriage ended in divorce and he became estranged from his children.

The intermittent wiper is now standard in all domestic and foreign cars thanks to the flash of genius of Bob Kearns.

28. KINGFISHERS BREAK SONIC BOOM FOR TRAINS

Advances in travel have us looking for ways to go faster and faster. Train travel seems to have finally caught up with technology. Unfortunately, the tremendous noise they make has outweighed the benefits. Some high-speed trains can sound like they are crashing through the sound barrier when they exit tunnels.

The problem is that as a train travels down a tunnel it compresses the air in front of it and the air coalesces. The coalesced air (shock wave) quickly expands to the surrounding areas and causes the air to rapidly accelerate and create a sonic boom, which sounds like an explosion.

There are two ways to reduce this sonic boom effect. You could change the tunnel geometry to relieve pressure, but it would be very costly to alter existing structures. The other option is to redesign the front of the train (where the problem begins as the coalesced air gathers). This is what engineers have done, and their inspiration was the kingfisher.

The kingfisher is a bird with a unique beak that can dive into water with hardly a splash. That's because the kingfisher's beak produces smaller shock waves and allows water to flow past it smoothly.

Mimicking the blunt shape of the kingfisher's beak on the front of the train produces a number of smaller weak shock waves, which alleviates the shock wave problem that came from the high speeds of the train barreling through the narrow tunnels.

As the train exits the tunnel, the lower strength shock waves on the front of the train do not have enough strength to produce the sonic boom felt by neighboring residents. These trains are faster, quieter, and use clean electricity while providing a great alternative to sitting in rush-hour traffic.

NASA performed a sonic boom demonstration on a modified Northrop Grumman F5. By altering the shape of the aircraft they were able to prove that they could control the shockwaves and sonic boom signature emanating from the aircraft. Planes and trains are beneficiaries of the knowledge gleaned from the kingfisher.

Flying behind and below the modified F-5E, and using its specially-instrumented nose boom, the F-15B recorded many shockwave patterns from the F-5E at various distances and orientations from the aircraft. (NASA photo by Carla Thomas)

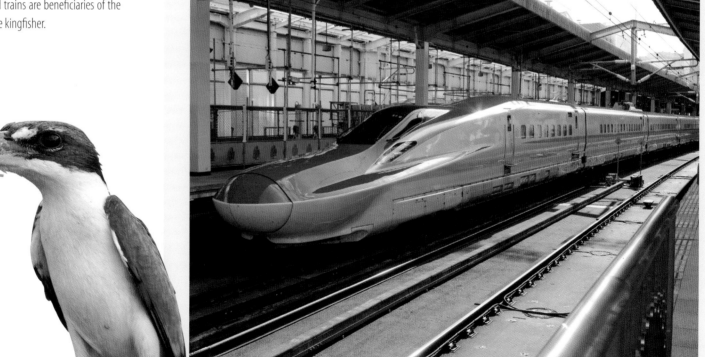

Science is an interesting beast, sometimes resembling a freight train or a bus in the slow lane. Not all scientific moments are "eureka" moments. Insignificant observations can be instrumental in ushering in new methods, new ideas, and pioneering new advances even when it is not immediately evident. Not all ideas are good ideas, but copying something proven to work gets you at least halfway there.

We have taken for granted how technology has changed so rapidly. It seems as if the new gadget you bought yesterday is obsolete today. Today we have access to almost unlimited information, thanks to the Internet. We can read and build on those who were there before us without doing the heavy lifting. We forget that things weren't always like that. There was a time when observation, trial, and error were the norm. Innovation was slower and more methodical.

Mark Isambard Brunel may not be a name you are familiar with, but he was an innovator who changed the face of how we travel. Brunel's story is also a fascinating one and reads like a Victorian novel.

A French-born engineer, Brunel was a staunch royalist, and in 1793 he fled the French Revolution to the United States and became a citizen and eventually the chief engineer of New York City. In 1799 he sailed to England and was commissioned to construct a tunnel under the Thames. England led the world in technology and industrialization in the Victorian Age.

Brunel drew his inspiration from the burrowing technique of a creature called shipworm (*Teredo navalis*). Up to this point, tunneling through soft material such as clay was

Early drawing of a shipworm shows the shell structure at one end; they are a type of saltwater clam that burrows into wood using the shell valves view. Inside the Thames Tunnel in London, constructed using Brunel's tunnelling shield discovery inspired by shipworms.

tricky, treacherous, and usually ended in tragedy. He marveled at how the *Teredo navalis* would bore through the timbers of a ship and yet was protected by a hard shell while it was tunneling.

The teredo is a mollusk, closer to a clam than a worm, and has a small shell on top like a helmet, which is used to chip away at the wood. The wood shavings are digested and expelled out the back end. What Brunel observed is that the teredo has a soft, elongated body, which it protected by secreting a calcareous tube lining, similar to a tunnel.

Brunel's "eureka" moment came when he conceived of a moveable support structure to support the tunnel walls. His tunneling shield resembled a rectangular, open-ended steel box, protecting workers from collapse and allowing them to dig safely.

Brunel was knighted in 1841 and honored for this engineering milestone. Tunneling machines have advanced quite a bit since Brunel's time. Instead of men at the front digging out the tunnel, it is now done by a rotating head with cutting wheels.

The tunnel, shield is now an integral part with the cutting head and provides the required tunnel support as the TBM (Tunnel Boring Machine) moves way down. The TBM has hydraulic jacks on its sides that are supported by the tunnel walls; these jacks are used to push the TBM forward like

an earthworm.

Brunel's tunnel shield is a device that has been used in updated designs or adapted in similar form for almost every major tunnel built in the last 180 years. We can travel in an underground subway or train thanks to Brunel's observations so many years ago. Perhaps Brunel's greatest contribution was his son, Isambard Kingdom Brunel, who would later be known as one of the greatest engineers in history. Isambard was second only to Winston Churchill according to a BBC poll of the 100 greatest Britons.

MOTH'S EYE INSPIRES NEW SOLAR CELLS

I remember watching a movie in the 1980s called *The Fly*. It was kind of a no-frills movie in its special effects and costuming. What struck me as odd were the strange, buggy eyes on the character who turned into a man/fly hybrid. The eyes looked low budget, not at all the multi-faceted type of eyes that we know that flies possess, but hey, it was the eighties and we went to the movies to be entertained, not educated.

The moth's eye is interestingly multi-faceted when observed with magnification. What would happen if you shone a light into a moth's eye? The rule of thumb is that light that projects on a surface at an angle is called the angle of incidence which results in:

Refraction OR	Light is absorbed; it passes through the surface and disappears.
Reflection OR	Light is reflected or bounced back and you see it.

A combination of both reflection and refraction

You would expect the moth's eye to reflect light like a mirrored funhouse due to the innumerable facets in the eye that resemble mirror panels, but the opposite is true. A moth's eye has zero reflection and 100 percent transmittance. This occurs when the angle of reflection is 90 degrees to the angle of refraction. This angle is known as "Brewster's angle."

Here is an example of Brewster's angle. Look at the window in the house below. The image on the left shows a reflection in the window. The image on the right of the same house shows no reflection in the window. The reason is that the angle of reflection is perpendicular to the angle of refraction.

If the light were shifted slightly it would be reflected (bounced toward you). Herein lies the secret of the moth's eye — the exterior tiny ridges and bumps that change the direction of the light. Each ridge does its part to ensure that no light is reflected. There is such an abundance of these ridges that they account for all perceivable angles that the light could hit on the surface of the eye, making the light seemingly disappear as if absorbed.

The ability to capture and absorb light arriving at different angles is fueling new discoveries in solar panels. Potentially, nanoparticles in a liquid suspension may be etched into panels to increase efficiency and decrease cost, propelling solar energy into the future.

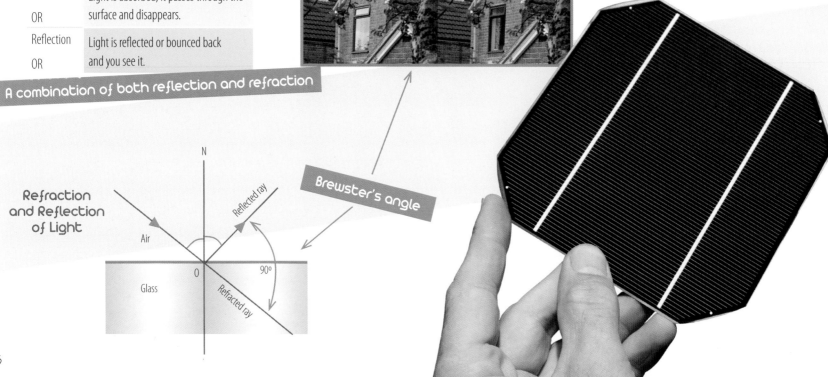

Refraction and Reflection of Light

N

Reflected ray

Air

Brewster's angle

0   90°

Glass

Refracted ray

Close-up of multi-faceted moth's eye

31. THE ASTONISHING LEAF AND POWER SUPPLIES

Dr. Daniel Nocera of MIT recently said, "A practical artificial leaf has been one of the Holy Grails of science for decades."[5] This is probably because the leaf seems as impossible to copy as the human brain. The capability of converting the energy of the sun into a storable energy in the form of sugars, through a process called photosynthesis, is astonishing enough to make you green with envy! The photosynthesis process is complex yet very efficient as it flawlessly moves through different stages to arrive with the stored energy.

The process has been understood for years, but never completely copied. Researchers are hoping to change that. A significant finding has been the replication of a very small portion of the photosynthesis process, but in a simplistic form. It is at the beginning of the process where water molecules are broken down to their basic components.

Water is made up of two parts hydrogen and one part oxygen — H_2O. Water is an abundant resource, which makes it desirable as an energy source. It has been a goal of scientists to efficiently separate these molecules in the way that natural photosynthesis processes it.

Currently, scientists can divide water into components through a process called electrolysis. Electrolysis needs an external power source such as a battery and two electrodes. The two electrodes are placed in water, with each electrode connected to the positive and negative terminals of the battery.

Once the battery is connected, current begins to flow to the two electrodes. This causes the water to separate the hydrogen and oxygen molecules down to their molecular level. The result is each element giving off gas bubbles. But this process is done with an external battery. It is not true photosynthesis that utilizes the sun's free and abundant energy.

The quest to obtain these gases has encouraged scientists to look at how the leaf initiates photosynthesis by using the sun's energy as the sole source to start this reaction. It starts with chloroplasts, the mechanism inside the leaf that triggers this reaction, but scientists are unable to replicate this mechanism so they began thinking outside the box to get off the starting block.

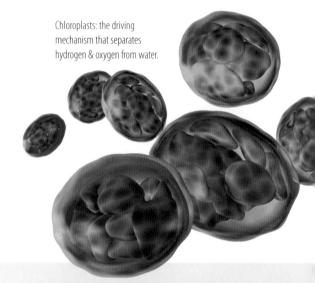

Chloroplasts: the driving mechanism that separates hydrogen & oxygen from water.

Dr. Nocera, who was mentioned earlier, came up with a clever concept. He sandwiched a thin sheet of semi-conducting silicon between a layer of cobalt and a layer of nickel-molybdenum-zinc alloy. The cobalt acts as a catalyst, which releases the oxygen. The nickel alloy side also acts as a catalyst and releases the hydrogen.

Cobalt > oxygen

Nickel alloy > hydrogen

This replication of the leaf is completely wireless and works by placing the artificial leaf in a container of water and exposing it to sunlight. In order for the gases to be useful, both gases need to be captured and stored. This is a technical hurdle due to the volatility of both gases in their basic form — particularly hydrogen, which if not handled correctly can be explosive (think hydrogen bomb).

Every step thereafter is currently out of reach, but photosynthesis has been touted as the next revolution in the green technology and independence from fossil fuels. This technical hurdle is motivating these researchers to go back to the drawing board.

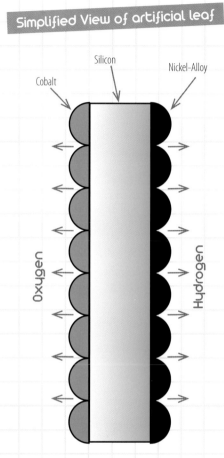

Simplified View of artificial leaf

Cobalt   Silicon   Nickel-Alloy

Oxygen   Hydrogen

32. MATHEMATICS, SUNFLOWERS, AND CATCHING SOME RAYS

Talk of solar energy has been around for as long as I can remember. The lure is understandable. The sun is a readily available source of great and seemingly unlimited power. We know that plants harness and store power systematically through photosynthesis by converting the light to energy, which is then converted to chemical energy and into food. This process did not escape the notice of researchers.

Solar-powered devices have been around for a long time. You may own a solar-powered device such as a light or calculator. The problem is not the technology but the size of the solar panels required when you want to harness vast amounts of energy. A lot of panels require a lot of land.

There are concentrated solar power (CSP) plants around the world. They consist of a central tower surrounded by giant mirrors (heliostats), each the size of half a tennis court. The mirrors reflect the sun's rays toward the tower, which in turn converts the rays to electricity through the use of steam turbines. The efficiency of a CSP plant is a measure of how effectively the sun's rays are reflected toward the tower throughout the course of the day.

Unfortunately, issues arose when adjacent mirrors were casting shadows or blocking the sun's rays. That problem arose at CSP Plant PS10 located just outside of Seville, Spain. CSP Plant PS10 consists of 624 heliostats (each 394 square feet, or 120 square meters, in size) and a 328-foot (100 m) tall tower.

To resolve that problem, science has once again turned to God's creation for a solution. What better place to look than the sunflower, which is known to flourish and seemingly follow the sun? Sunflowers are beautiful to behold, but what caught the eye of researchers at MIT, in collaboration with RWTH Aachen University in Germany, was their central spiral pattern.

The florets are arranged in a geometric spiral pattern starting from the center and working outward. Each successive floret is placed 137.5 degrees from the previous one, resulting in a mesmerizing design known as a Fermat spiral. The 137.5 degrees is a very special angle known as the golden angle (or golden ratio), which minimizes shadows and blockage while maximizing exposure to the sun's rays.

Mathematically applying the golden angle to the PS10 arrangement resulted in an astounding 20 percent reduction in the footprint, plus the bonus of increased solar efficiency. It works out that the golden angle is related to a numerical sequence called the Fibonacci numbers, which is a sequence of numbers where each numeral is the sum of the two previous ones: 0, 1, 1, 2, 3, 5, 8, 13, 21, 34, 55, 89, 144, and so on.

For you math lovers, here is how this sequence works:

0
$0 + 1 = 1$
$1 + 1 = 2$
$2 + 1 = 3$
$2 + 3 = 5$

When you count the number of spirals in the sunflower, you will notice that the number that you count both clockwise and counter-clockwise is actually the Fibonacci numbers. A closer look at the golden angle of 137.5 degrees reveals that if you were to relate this angle to a ratio of a complete revolution (one revolution is 360 degrees) you'd get: 137.5 / 360 = .382, or 222.5 degrees with a corresponding ratio of .618 revolutions.

Fibonacci numbers & the golden angle (ratio)

If we calculate the ratios of successive numbers you will notice that they eventually settle down to 1.618, which is called the golden ratio; where the 1.618 would be equivalent in saying that the angle is 360 (1) + 222.5 (.618) = 582.5 degrees (222.5 degrees, which is equivalent to 137.5 degrees). This is the connection between the Fibonacci numbers and the golden angle.

Phyllotaxis and the golden angle

If you want to observe how this applies you may want to visit this website: http://www.mathisfun.com/numbers/nature-golden-ratio-fibonacci.html.

The golden angle plays a significant role in phyllotaxis. Phyllotaxis is the arrangement of leaves on a plant stem, and the golden angle and its function is to:

- provide plants with maximum light exposure

- cast a minimal shadow on adjacent leaves

- provide the best possible exposure for falling rain to flow down the stem to the roots;

- arrange petals for the best possible exposure to insects to pollination.

God, in His infinite brilliance, has bestowed this golden angle throughout the plant population so that His creation would thrive.

The earth brought forth vegetation, plants yielding seed according to their own kinds, and trees bearing fruit in which is their seed, each according to its kind. And God saw that it was good (Genesis 1:11).

The solar array in Seville, Spain

CONCLUSION

We can't live without water. It covers 97 percent of the earth in the form of saltwater oceans, and yet, as much as we would like to, we can't drink it or even use it for crops. Drinkable water for the billions on the earth only amounts to 3 percent of the total amount. But 2 percent of that is shut up in the form of ice on the polar caps, so that leaves just 1 percent of the earth's water available to sustain all the life on earth. This fresh water sits in lakes, ponds, rivers, streams, and deposits beneath the soil.

However, there is one other place in which vast amounts of fresh drinkable water are stored. Trillions upon trillions of tons of water sit above us in the form of pregnant puffy clouds, waiting for their waters to break. These great water deposits float like feathers above our heads, and they do so because of fixed laws.

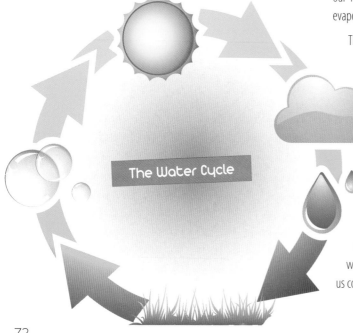

The Water Cycle

The water gets there because of an incredible process called "the water cycle." This process happens when the waters of the earth change from their heavy liquid form and become water vapor. As the sun heats the water, it rises and forms itself into lighter-than-air water deposits we call clouds.

As this happens, salt and impurities are left behind on the earth so that we can have a supply of salt to give taste to our food, as well as drinkable water, which, before the evaporation process, was pestilential.

The clouds sit above us, storing trillions of tons of clean, life-giving, fresh drinking water. This water is placed between 10,000 and 20,000 feet in the sky, and if it wasn't for the process of condensation, that's where it would all stay, and we would all eventually die of thirst. Condensation is the opposite of evaporation. It occurs when the gases that transported the water to the clouds because of heat form back into water because of cold. This cooler temperature causes the gas to form into drops and then drop (or drip) so that we can have crops from the drops and drink cool fresh water. This process is called "precipitation," or "rain" for us common folks.

The rain falls to the earth, is collected in lakes, rivers, and streams, and because of the existence of gravity, eventually finds itself transported into the vast oceans where it evaporates, is cleansed, and falls again. This means that water never really disappears down the drain. Thank God, it comes back to us so that we can live.

Copying God's Water Cycle

So it seems that the water cycle is simple. Heat and drink. In other words, we could easily copy God's water cycle and create fresh water from salt water by heating salt water and catching it.

"In April 2000 the Texas Water Development Board approved a $59,000 grant to the Lavaca-Navadid River Authority to determine if building a $400 million plant on Matagorda Bay at Point Comfort would be economically and environmentally feasible. There is a power plant at this location that could supply the heated sea water for the membrane process. The study was released two months later and the cost rose to $755 million, but that included the cost of transmission facilities to San Antonio."[6]

SAWS president and CEO Robert Puente said, "That's finance science fiction today." Ocean water desalination is extraordinarily expensive — more than ten times the cost of aquifer water. A plant and pipeline would cost well over $1 billion in today's dollars. [7]

Look at the incredible cost — simply to copy what God makes available to us at no charge.

God said to Job, "Have you comprehended the breadth of the earth? Tell me, if you know all this" (Job 38:18). The year was around 2000 B.C. Job wasn't a "know-it-all." He had no idea as to the size of the earth upon which he lived, and not until comparatively recent years in man's history have we been able to comprehend the breadth of the earth. Here's a little trivia to show us the size of the huge earth: It took four years, 21 million steps, and 22 pairs of leather shoes for Dave Kunst to complete his record-making 14,450–mile walk around the earth back in 1974. But if by breadth the Scriptures mean the widest part of the earth, if you were to walk along the equator (across water) at 3 mph without a break, it would take 8,333 hours. Even with these thoughts, it's difficult to comprehend the breadth of the earth, until you fly high in a plane and gaze at the vast and distant horizon.

God also speaks of the sea's springs: "Have you entered into the springs of the sea, or walked in the recesses of the deep?" (Job 38:16). For most of human history we have been in the dark about the depth of the oceans or even that there were "springs" in the sea that sent out water into the ocean.

"In many areas of the ocean floor, wherever magma nears the seafloor, or where lava erupts directly at the seafloor surface, hot springs on the seafloor called hydrothermal vents commonly are found. Vent fields are generally as-

Hydrothermal Vents

sociated with submarine (undersea) volcanoes where lava is erupting or preparing to erupt. The average temperature of deep ocean water is only 2°C (36°F). The water coming directly from a hydrothermal vent can reach up to 350°C (662°F) and is rich in dissolved chemicals. The hot spring water forms a plume above the vent, somewhat like smoke rising from a chimney into the air. Temperature-sensing instruments, towed behind research vessels, can detect these hot-water plumes and aid oceanographers in locating hydrothermal vents on the ocean floor. "[8]

The discovery of hydrothermal vents in the mid-1970s constitutes one of the great advances of science in the 20th century. The study of hydrothermal vents and their attendant animal communities is a new frontier for oceanographers and one of the last unexplored regions on earth. With each research dive, new species are discovered and new information comes to light. [9]

Look now at the secret world of the snowflake: "Hast thou entered into the treasures of the snow? Or has thou seen the treasures of the hail, which I have reserved against the

Snowflake photos by Wilson Bentley. Bentley was a bachelor farmer whose hobby was photographing snowflakes. Winter 1902.

time of trouble, against the day of battle and war?" (Job 38:22–23; KJV).

There are four basic shapes of snowflakes:

Stellar dendrite snowflakes are the most common. The word stellar means "star-like" and dendrite means "tree-like." They have the appearance of stars that have tiny "branches."

Hexagonal plate snowflakes are very thin and are made of solid ice, looking like a dinner plate with six sides.

Column snowflakes are longer and thinner, looking similar to the columns found on buildings. Each column snowflake has six sides.

Needle snowflakes are extremely thin and long and look very much like needles, once again having six sides.

God asks Job if he has entered into the treasures of the snow. This is a very strange question, because snow may look nice for a day or so as it covers the ground, but it seems inappropriate to call a snowflake or hail a "treasure." It wasn't until the advent of the telescope that man was able to "enter" into another world and see the incredible design of the snowflake and of hail, and begin to comprehend how many there are and the differences in design, revealing breathtaking symmetry. That didn't happen until after 1590, when a couple of eyeglass makers (Zaccharias Janssen and son Hans Janssen) put multiple lenses in a tube and noticed that objects that were placed in front of the tube looked bigger. This was, in essence, the first microscope.

In 1885, Wilson Alwyn Bentley photographed thousands of snowflakes in an attempt to see if he could find two that were identical, but each one was distinctive in design. Every snowflake is not only a treasure of beauty, but it is unique in its individual design, giving us a glimpse of the unspeakably incredible mind of God.

"This stuff falls out of the sky and we don't know how it works and we're naturally curious," said Kenneth Libbrecht, professor of physics at California Institute of Technology. Studying snowflakes, Libbrecht points out, is strictly for curiosity's sake. The discovery of why each flake is unique is not expected to have much of an impact on anything. The effort to learn about snowflakes is kind of like brain candy. Indeed, many great minds have applied themselves to finding out why, such as philosopher Renè Descartes and nuclear physicist Ukichiro Nakaya. Still, no concrete answer.[10]

Suddenly, God moved from natural truths to the big issue. He asked Job, "Have the gates of death been revealed to you? Or have you seen the gates of deep darkness?" (Job 38:17). Back when I was 20 years old, I began to think deeply about the meaning of life and death, and came up with nothing. I searched and came to the nightmare conclusion that life had no meaning and death had no solution. There seemed to be no way around this terrible dark door that each of us must face. Such a thought left me in quiet despair.

What's In a Name?

One dark night in April of 1972, God reached down and gave me light in my darkness. He brought comfort to my pained and thirsty soul. He gave me an alternative door (see John 10:9) and used a surfing buddy named Graeme Reid to share the gospel with me. That night I came out of darkness into light — out of death into life. Please let me have the honor of sharing that same gospel with you.

The complexity and order of creation tells us that there is a Creator, and we intuitively know that this Creator is good, and that He requires us to be good. If God therefore is good, He must demand that there be ultimate justice. There must be retribution for crimes of murder and rape, torture and cruelty. To think otherwise is to think that Almighty God is not good — that He's unjust, and in doing so we become guilty of the sin of idolatry - making up a false god. Besides, if there is no hell, then the Bible has led us to believe a lie, and Jesus is therefore a false prophet and Christians are bearing false witness. Rather, we see that the Scriptures speak of its existence many times, and as we have just seen, the Bible proves itself to be supernatural in origin. If it wasn't the Word of God, it wouldn't contain then unknown scientific truths. So we must listen to what it says and heed its fearsome warnings.

With those thoughts in mind, think of what pleases you in life. Do you enjoy a glass of cool water on a hot day, or a tender steak when you are really hungry? Or do you marvel when a hummingbird comes close to you, or when you see a massive white puffy cloud set in a deep blue sky? Imagine if hell was simply the removal of those things. Imagine experiencing thirst but never being able to quench its insatiable yearning, or experiencing the unending pains of hunger. Imagine if God is as perfect as the Bible warns that He is, and that He means what He says about the Day of Justice. Imagine dying in your sins and not only having pleasure removed, but "just" punishment inflicted.

Our imagination can give us pleasure and it can help us to avoid pain. We can imagine what it would be like to be electrocuted, fall off a cliff, drown, or be murdered. Such fearful thoughts make us careful around electricity, heights, water, and dangerous places and people. Yet a place called "hell" cannot simply be imagined. We can read about it again and again in Holy Scripture.

Earlier, we looked closely at the tiny ant, but in studying the ant we can easily forget that God also created the massive sun. Did you know that the earth could fit into the volume of the sun over a million times? Think of it . . . what sort of Being could create the sun? Its Creator says, "I the LORD search the heart and test the mind, to give every man according to his ways, according to the fruit of his deeds" (Jeremiah 17:10). How will you do on that day when your Maker judges the world in righteousness? Have you kept the Ten Commandments? Let's go through a few of them to see how you will do.

How many lies do you think you have told in your whole life? Take an estimate. How many things do you think that

you have stolen (regardless of value)? Search your memory banks. Listen to the voice of your conscience and let it do its God-given duty. Have you ever used God's name in vain? If you have, then let me ask you a few questions. Do you believe that He gave you your life? Are you thankful? If you say that you are then I have to ask why you have used His holy name as a cuss word. That sin is called "blasphemy," and under God's law it is so serious it merits the death sentence. But our sinfulness goes even deeper. God sees our thought-life. Look at what Jesus said about that: Whoever looks at a woman to lust for her has already committed adultery with her in his heart (Matthew 5:28).

Have you ever looked with lust at another person? You have to face God. Alone. On Judgment Day. That's a scary thought for a guilty sinner. The Bible warns that it's a "fearful thing to fall into the hands of the living God" (Hebrews 10:31).

So let your imagination work for your good and think for a moment about the terrors of Judgment Day. But don't let that be your primary reason for calling on the mercy of God. You don't need the Savior to save you from hell — you need Him to save you from sin. This is because our repentance must be soaked with contrition. We must be sorry for sinning against Him, and to be sorry we must see our sins in their true light. This is why we need the Ten Commandments. They show us the holiness of God and the sinfulness of our hearts. I had no idea how sinful I was until I was confronted with the knowledge that God saw lust as adultery (see Matthew 5:27–28), or that "lying lips are an abomination to the LORD" (Proverbs 12:22). He is perfect and holy, and His justice therefore demands perfect retribution.

Imagine being found guilty of being a lying, thieving, blasphemous adulterer-at-heart on that Day. Please, be

honestly brutal with yourself. Listen to your conscience as it reminds you of past hidden sins . . . and then think about the reality of that terrible place called hell. The strong consolation is that God doesn't want you to end up there, but as sure as hell that's where you will go if you die without His forgiveness. Justice must be served.

Brought to Christ

God's law (the Ten Commandments) is our enemy, because we have violated its perfect precepts. We are like criminals who are running from the law. Every time we sin, we store up its wrath. The Bible tells us that God's law is not only perfect, but it's holy, just, and good. So its holy indignation justly abides on each of us (see John 3:36). It should instantly prosecute us and damn us to Hell. But the Scriptures tell us that because God is rich in mercy He has temporarily held back His wrath and let the Law act as a "schoolmaster." Its purpose is "to bring us to Christ" (see Galatians 3:24). Look at what God did so that we could have mercy rather than justice! He became a man (in Jesus Christ) and suffered and died on the cross, taking our punishment upon Himself. We broke the Law, and Jesus paid our fine: "For God so loved the world that He gave His only begotten Son, that whoever believes in Him should not perish but have everlasting life" (John 3:16). Then Jesus rose from the grave and defeated death. That means you can be legally dismissed from the courtroom and be given everlasting life. Your death sentence can be commuted. God will forgive you, justify you (make it as though you had never sinned), and give you the righteousness of Jesus Christ. So repent today (turn from all sin), and trust alone in Jesus Christ for your eternal salvation. Please do it right now! Trust Him as you would trust a parachute to save you. Do what the

Scriptures say to do: "Put on the Lord Jesus Christ" and do it today. . . because you may not have tomorrow.

Pray something like this: "Dear God, I am so sorry for my sins against You. Please forgive me. From this day I will trust Jesus Christ alone as my Lord and Savior. In His Name I pray, Amen." Now read the Bible daily, and obey what you read.

Always keep in mind that God loves and values us, but our value to Him isn't drawn out because we are loveable, but because God is the reservoir of love. There's nothing desirable in us, and yet God set His desire upon us. It is in that sense that we are of value and can have a sense

of tremendous dignity. We are not beasts, but creatures made in the image of God. It is upon that understanding that we have promises such as "He who did not spare His own Son, but delivered Him up for us all, how shall He not with Him also freely give us all things?" (Romans 8:32). The cross was "for us," such is our value in His sight. That means that your acceptance with Him never has to be earned. You don't have to strive to please Him. Just trust and obey. That means do everything from now on making sure that you have God's smile. Please feel free to go to www.livingwaters.com and read "Save Yourself Some Pain" for principles of Christian growth.

ENDNOTES

1   Nigel R. Franks and Tom Richardson, "Teaching in Tandem-running Ants," Nature 439 (7073) (January 12, 2006): p. 153.

2   Singh AV et al. Bio-inspired approaches to design smart fabrics. J Mater Design (2011), doi:10.1016/j.matdes.2011.01.061

2   "Mantis Shrimp Eyes Might Inspire New High-Def Devices," Wired Science, October 26, 2009; http://www.wired.com/wired-science/2009/10/mantis-shrimp-eyes/.

3   "Brightly Colored Bird Feathers Inspire New Kind of Laser," Wired Science, May 6, 2011; http://www.wired.com/wiredscience/2011/05/biomimetic-laser/.

4   Daniel Nocera et al, 241st National Meeting of the American Chemical Society, March 27–31, 2011, Anaheim, California; http://blogs.discovermagazine.com/80beats/2011/03/28/scientists-create-worlds-1st-practical-artificial-leaf-10x-as-efficient-as-the-real-thing/

5   http://www.edwardsaquifer.net/desalination.html.

6   "S.A. Urged to Look to Gulf for More Water," San Antonio Express-News, March 10, 2010.

7   http://www.waterencyclopedia.com/Ge-Hy/Hot-Springs-on-the-Ocean-Floor.html.

8   Ibid.

9   "What Makes a Snowflake Unique?" http://www.wired.com/science/discoveries/news/2001/02/41085

PHOTO CREDITS: T-top, B-bottom, L-left, R-right, C-Center

A BRAVE NEW WORLD – DEFINING THE NEW SCIENCES

Architectural Bionics – A new trend in architecture that incorporates inspiration from the natural world into functional architecture through the observation of the natural world along with mathematics, structure and efficiency. It blends the disciplines of architecture with bionic and civil and structural engineering.

Bioengineering – The manipulation of biological systems toward the application of new engineering principles from conception of design, analysis, and production.

Biomaterial Science – Biomaterial scientists and engineers study cells, tissues, and organs as they interact with materials both natural and synthetic.

Biomimicry & Biomimetics – The copying and application of ideas and inspiration from the fields of biology to technology. Researchers use observable nature to inspire new designs, and improve or provide sustainable solutions for engineers, materials science, medicine and manufacturers.

Biomorphic – Resemblance of a living organism in shape or appearance. This would include robots with resemblance to insects, animals, humans, etc.

Bionics/Technical Bionics – A broad area of science that gathers information about the functioning of biological systems toward the development of new technologies. Technical bionics examines and applies these towards engineering tasks. Etymology of the word comes from *bi* (as in life) + *onics* (as in electronics).

Composite Structure – A combination of different materials layered together to form a single structure.

Homology – This is a biologists' attempt to explain to how similar forms fulfill different functions. For example, a whale's fins and bats' wings are structurally similar yet perform different functions.

Macromolecular Science – The study of the synthesis, structure, processing, properties and use of natural and synthetic materials known as polymers.

Materials Engineering & Science – These engineers and scientists are responsible for the development, processing, and testing of materials to create new and innovative materials systems. They determine how different materials interact with each other.

Metamaterials – Metamaterials are composite systems whose properties are dominated not by the individual atoms but by the properties of larger, artificially produced structures or "meta-atoms."

Molecular Biology – The field of molecular biology studies macromolecules and the macromolecular mechanisms found in living things. It works to rework, mutate or replicate with interesting results.

Nano - measurement – In general nanotechnology is expressed in nanometers (1 nm = 10^{-9} m) length units. There are 25,400,000 nanometers in one inch. Although many cite the nano, it does not exclusively imply the measurement but can also be used to describe something very small or minuscule as in nanobots (internal medical robots).

Nanotechnology – The science and technology of creating and building devices with the use of single atoms and molecules, one by one.

Nano BioSystems – This is the widely used term when referring to numerous medical applications.

Reverse Engineering – Simply put, it is the attempt to copy what is already designed and exists. It is working backwards by dismantling and reassembling to see the why and how something works and replicate it. This is usually the discipline when studying natural and biological specimens like cells or animals. However, it can be the stealing of one man-made design to make the same design, such as spies who steal aircraft plans to make a similar aircraft.

Tribology – The science and technology of friction, lubrication, and wear of interacting surfaces in relative motion.

Quantum Mechanics – A theory of matter that is based on the concept of the possession of wave properties by elementary particles, that affords a mathematical interpretation of the structure and interactions of matter on the basis of these properties, and that incorporates within it quantum theory and the uncertainty principle —called also wave mechanics.

Quantum Revolution – The quantum revolution started in the early 1900s with Planck & Einstein to explain the behavior of atoms, molecules, and nuclei. It has grown and been added to by a number of researchers who developed theories to add to the rules that govern physical reality. It may appear as though it can only be understood by the scientific elite with obfuscating jargon. Statements such as "the rules of quantum mechanics state that given two unknowns, it is only ever possible to specify one at a time and both cannot be known simultaneously" would seem like double talk. It is hoped by scientists that the quantum revolution will develop new technologies and even shape the world with these variables that cannot be fully understood.

AUTHOR **BIOS**

Ray Comfort is a best-selling author of more than 70 books, and television co-host (with actor, Kirk Cameron) of the award-winning program "The Way of the Master." Please visit www.livingwaters.com for a complete selection of his books, audios, DVD's, tracts, and free material to help you grow in your faith.

Jeffrey Seto works as an aerospace engineer in experimental research and development. His work encompasses supersonic boom suppression, synthetic vision approach systems and structural and system testing in civilian and military sectors.

Jeffrey has worked internationally in the U.S, Canada and Germany for over 20 years. He holds a B.Eng in aerospace, an electrical engineering diploma in avionics and is a senior member of AIAA (American Institute of Aeronautics and Astronautics). He is married and currently resides in California.